# IF
# SYMPTOMS
# PERSIST

# IF
# SYMPTOMS
# PERSIST

## Theodore Dalrymple

## Illustrations by Nick Newman

ANDRE DEUTSCH

The following articles all appeared in *The Spectator*
between 1991 and 1994

First published in Great Britain in 1994 by
André Deutsch Limited
106 Great Russell Street
London WC1B 3LJ

CIP data for this title is available
from the British Library

ISBN 0 233 98898 X

Printed in Great Britain by
WBC, Bridgend

# Foreword

It is now more than four years since Dominic Lawson, then newly-appointed as editor, asked me whether I would write a weekly medical column in *The Spectator*. He did not want a column of advice to readers as to what they should do if they had spots or a raised level of molybdenum in their blood, such as is available from the hypochondriac's page of every daily newspaper; no, he wanted a chronicle of life in the raw. Working in an enormous slum, and visiting prison often, I was in a position to provide it.

I have always preferred ministering to the poor than to the rich. This is not because I am seized with missionary zeal, or a burning desire to do good: it is simply that the problems of the poor are so much more interesting to me than those of the rich. And if I have been able in my column to inform the rich about the existence their poorer fellow-citizens lead only a few miles from them, but who might as well be on the dark side of the moon for all the contact they have with them, I shall have performed a small public service.

For, having worked in several countries of the so-called Third World, and having travelled extensively through all the continents, I am convinced that the poverty of spirit to be found in an English slum is the worst to be found anywhere. More flagrant injustices by far, worse physical conditions, greater exposure to violence, are of course to be encountered elsewhere: but for sheer apathy, for spiritual, emotional, educational and cultural nihilism and vacuity, you must go to an English slum.

Nowhere in the world – at least in my experience – are people to be found who have so little feeling of control over, or responsibility for, their own lives and behaviour. Indeed, patients often speak to me of the course of their life as if it were totally unconnected with what they themselves had done. Often they talk, incoherently, of an immaculate self, untouched by human conduct: the psychobabble of the slums. Not surprisingly, they are awaiting a political or economic dispensation which will relieve them of their woes. *They* – the Social, the doctor, the Housing, the Council – will make them whole. This is an illusion which politicians are all too happy to foster, for it increases their self-importance and wins votes.

I am not speaking of a tiny ghetto, an island of despairing passivity off a continent of hopeful activity. I am speaking of a considerable proportion of our population. After all, foreigners often remark that half of England looks like a slum, whatever the figures for the GDP per head may say; and its people look crushed and defeated. Forty million foreigners can't be wrong.

But crushed and defeated by what, exactly? I have my theories, but this is not the place to expound them. The first step is to admit the phenomena, which is a painful enough process: for, as any doctor knows, the patient often strenuously denies his symptoms. He wants to believe that nothing has happened to him, that he can carry on in the same old way.

# 1

The lilies of the field, which neither toil nor spin, enjoy one decisive advantage: they photosynthesise. This means that they have only to put forth leaves into the sunlight and the carbon dioxide to be assured of a decent living. Man, alas, must work to live; and even the unemployed have to visit the Department of Social Security, which is undoubtedly labour of a kind (our local office is like a battleground).

It is unusual to come across someone from the inner city who takes literally Christ's injunction to spare no thought for the morrow, but over the past few weeks I have been seeing a man who did just that, with consequences which he now considers disastrous.

His parents were religious, in a narrow sectarian way, and early instilled in him a horror of pleasure and a crushing sense of guilt. Happiness was theologically suspect, and from the age of eight he began to have nightmares that he had committed the sin which was without forgiveness, either in this world or the next.

Nevertheless, he was destined for a normal and respectable career. He wanted to be a teacher, like his parents. At college, however, he had a religious crisis. One Sunday he went to church and realised that no one in the congregation was following Christ's teaching to the letter. He went out, sold his car, his stereo equipment and his camera, and gave the proceeds away.

Unfortunately, he soon discovered that it is not easy to be a lily of the field in a slum. News of his generosity spread fast and he was quickly inundated by requests for funds from alcoholics, drug addicts and the like. When the funds ran out, requests were followed by threats, and threats by bricks through the window. Before long, he moved out of his flat, persuading himself that he was doing so to be more like unto the birds of the air. Now, ten years later, he reinterpreted his motive as sheer cowardice.

Thenceforth, he lived peripatetically, a night with a friend here, a night in a doorway there. He so despised the world and its ways of compromise that he refused even to go to the dentist, and his teeth fell out. He spent his days chatting with down-and-outs, the unemployed, the flotsam and jetsam who inhabit slum cafés, whom he took for the meek of the Sermon on the Mount, and he considered himself morally superior to all those impure beings who sullied their souls by working for lucre in Thatcher's Britain. Ten years later, he reinterpreted his behaviour as arrogance and laziness.

Now, after all this time, he had seen the error of his ways, and wanted to rejoin society. I gave him Edmund Gosse's *Father and Son* to read, but he found it too painfully apposite to complete. Every week, we wrestle in my consulting room with the philosophical question of how a man should act. True to his upbringing, he believes himself beyond redemption. I tell him that the difference between a man and an animal is that a man constantly re-invents himself. And, in part, I believe it.

'You've come to the top of the
waiting list.'

# 2

Symptoms are like bad husbands and wives: people will go to any length to be rid of them but, once gone, they miss them terribly. The result is that the symptoms return in new and worse forms, as do the rejected spouses. In human affairs, the general rule is once bitten, twice bitten.

Young and inexperienced doctors think of symptoms as the enemy, to be vanquished without mercy, but older and wiser doctors know that one's enemy's enemy is often not one's friend. Illness has its advantages and its privileges, and the doctor is well-advised to remember this before resorting to what is known as the therapeutic armamentarium.

A few weeks ago, I admitted a middle-aged lady to my ward who had been unable to walk for about two years, since her husband became a cardiac invalid after several heart attacks. Her ankle turned inwards, as in club foot, but the deformity corresponded to no pathology in her nerves, muscles or bones. In short, it was psychological in origin.

She and her family had plagued her general practitioner twice a week about her foot and eventually – in despair himself – he sent her to me. I admitted her to hospital, and gave instructions to the nurses that she was to be stood up straight, with her foot in the correct position. This achieved, they were to encourage her to walk, without a stick. By means of great care and devotion, she was soon rendered fully ambulant, and there was jubilation all round.

Well, not quite all round. She herself began to suffer from headaches and dizzy turns. ('I get these heads, doctor.') A battle of wills was about to commence, in the course of which I studiously ignored her 'heads' and all other complaints. But since factitiously ill patients are not immortal, they ultimately have a great advantage: if persistent enough, they will produce a symptom to alarm their doctor. In the war between hypochondriacs and hysterics on the one hand, and the medical profession on the other, nature herself and medico-legal considerations combine on the side of the former.

While my patient was in hospital, I formed some idea of the reasons for her mind-induced disability. She had brought up six children, by hand as Mrs Gargery would have put it, all of whom had now flown the parental nest. At precisely the moment when she might have expected a little relief from domestic drudgery, her husband, with whom her relations had always been difficult, became utterly helpless, in need of nursing day and night. What more logical than to become helpless herself?

As it happened, her 'illness' suited one of her daughters very well. She was married to a man whom she could not stand but whom, for religious reasons, she could not divorce. The need of both her parents for care and attention gave her an excuse to escape her husband.

If the mother's illness was so convenient both for herself and her daughter, why did they so assiduously seek a cure? Because they needed to disguise from themselves that the convenience of the illness was its cause. In curing the mother's disability, I have paved the way for disaster.

# 3

At the end of the consultation my patient took a small manila envelope from her handbag and slid it diffidently across my desk.

'I'm so grateful for what you've done, doctor,' she said, 'I'd like to buy you something for the hospital.'

Gratitude! It's the last thing I expected: you could have knocked me down with – well, with a small manila envelope.

I tore it open as soon as she left. It contained £5. Her donation reminded me of one of the handsomest gifts I ever received. I had treated an old African villager for malaria, and he returned soon afterwards with a small plastic bowl filled with sawdust in which nestled five eggs, very precious in those times of near-famine. His humility shamed me.

I should have bought something for my ward with the £5, of course, but the devil entered me and I decided to go through the proper channels. I called the administrator: his secretary answered.

'He's at a meeting,' she said. 'Can I be of help?'

I explained the situation and asked what I should do with the money.

'Well, we'll have to send an acknowledgment, of course,' she said. 'That's routine. But I'm not sure what we do with the money in a case like this. I'll have to ask the administrator when he returns from the meeting. Can I have the name, address and date of birth of the donor?'

It took me a few minutes to dictate them. The cost of the acknowledgment was rising.

Three hours later, the administrator's secretary called me.

'The administrator's spoken to the accountant,' she said. 'And he says the money'll have to go through the books.'

'Why?' I asked.

'Well, you see, if we write an acknowledgment – which we must – someone going through the files might ask where the £5 got to. Besides, the patient really gave the money to the whole hospital, not just your ward.'

'So we have to divide it up?'

'Yes, we do.'

There are twenty-four wards in the hospital: they will each receive twenty-one pence – less administrative expenses, of course.

'Could you pop the money in an envelope with a covering letter and send it here in the internal post?' asked the secretary.

It once took fourteen days for a referral letter to reach Ward 8 from Ward 11 through the internal post.

'Certainly,' I said. 'A pleasure.'

I dictated the covering letter: it took only ten minutes of my secretary's time. I'm sure it didn't take long to file, or alternatively to lose.

As for the £5, it will in due course be paid into the bank. The covering letter won't take long to write.

So far, then, my patient's little gift has cost the hospital quite a lot of money. If you add my time, the administrator's and the accountant's time, my secretary's time and the administrator's secretary's time, the postage and stationery, I estimate that my patient owes the hospital about £175, or £7.56 per ward.

It's lucky for her that it's the thought that counts.

'If you've a complaint about paperwork,
you should put it in writing.'

# 4

I was on duty at the prison last weekend. All was calm and quiet: as I inspected the kitchens (I'm still not quite sure what for), a rapist offered me the apple crumble for which he is famous throughout D wing. Just about edible when it leaves the kitchen, the crumble arrives in the wing as appetising as a ragout of old socks. As the French ask of good Scots porridge, 'Does one eat it, or has one eaten it?'

There were only two patients for me to see, so different yet so similar. The first, Bill, was a petty criminal with whom the courts had finally lost patience and sent down for a long time. Apart from housebreaking, Bill has one interest in life: swallowing razor-blades. If he has done it once, he has done it a hundred times. I've given up asking why: he always says, 'If I knew that, doctor, I'd stop.' This, of course, is the central misconception of psychotherapy, a misconception which has filtered its way down into the underworld.

Of late, Bill has developed a new interest: pushing wires through his abdominal wall into what we doctors call his guts. There is now a suppurating fistula whose characteristics I shall not describe, except to say that they are aesthetically unpleasing.

It is amazing how Bill can find a wire to push into himself, even when placed in a cell completely devoid of metal of any kind. I'm beginning to suspect the other prisoners smuggle wires to him: there's a black market for everything on the in.

Then there was Fred, a failed murderer. Fred had come to the conclusion that everything was the fault of the orforities, and had therefore written to his former probation officer threatening – in almost Magwitchian terms – to kill him on his release from prison.

9

The governor asked me to do something about Fred. I had a copy of the letter he had written before me, and it was enough to make one's blood curdle. (I refer, of course, to the orthography.)

'You, you basterd, did my hed in wen I was vunrable.' I confess that at this point I thought of the Vunrable Bede, who died in Jarrow in AD 776. Fred wrote that he would cut the probation officer's throat, but if he went to the police with the letter he would die a far more horrible death, by a means sure and lingering, but otherwise unspecified.

Among other allegations in the letter, Fred asserted that the probation officer had so done his head in that he had been reduced to swallowing razor-blades.

'How could he have done that?' I asked.

'Well, he's an orfority, isn't he?'

What wonderful totalitarians we British would make, I mused as I wrote my recommendation to the governor that Fred be prosecuted for uttering a threat to kill, contrary to some Act or other. How eager we are to ascribe our behaviour to others! I glanced in Fred's medical notes. The last entry was, 'Still has difficulty in making relationships.'

# 5

I sometimes wonder what patients think their insides are made of. Last week, an elderly lady of the mildest appearance informed me that her doctor had diagnosed a hiatus hyaena. I'd heard of the ravening beast within, of course, but this was absurd. What carnivore, red in tooth and claw, would be satisfied with mere antacids? I advised plenty of meat.

My next patient was a man with a plethoric face, who looked as though he spent his spare time writing angry letters to his local newspaper.

'Typical hospital,' he said as he came through the door of my room. 'Hundreds of people waiting for hours and nowhere to park your car.'

Having heard on the highest authority that a soft answer turns away wrath, I apologised for any inconvenience, but pointed out that I was seeing him exactly at the time of his appointment.

'Yes,' he said, 'but what about my next appointment? More than likely I'll have to wait for hours then.'

This is an example of what is known technically as anticipatory anxiety: worrying about something before it has happened. Anxiety, of course, is one of the many ways of giving meaning to life: it fills an existential void. As we know, the void is vast, while matter is but a trifle.

After my clinic I went to the ward where those who have tried to commit suicide, or at least have taken overdoses, are treated. A lady there had swallowed a bottle of pain-killers because her husband habitually gambled all their money away, leaving none with which to buy food for their three children or to pay the bills. If she tried to conceal money from him, he beat her. The overdose, however, was a turning point.

She was going to divorce her husband and live happily ever after.

'I've realised, doctor,' she said, 'that life's not worth killing yourself for.'

Amen to that.

At lunchtime, there was a meeting with the administrators. I go to such meetings only to pick up the latest management jargon and to savour the wilder flights of fatuity. One of my colleagues complained at the meeting that black bags of rubbish – seventeen at the last count – had accumulated in the last two weeks outside his ward. The General Services Manager (a janitor in a suit) replied that he was dedicated to providing a high-quality service but was acting under severe financial constraints. The General Manager (Clinical Services) interjected: 'Quality doesn't cost anything – and anyway, you can have too much of it.'

In the circumstances, one turns to the medical students for light relief.

Another colleague of mine, a specialist in the new and expanding but somewhat lugubrious field of terminal care, complained after the meeting that medical students these days were frivolous and had narrow horizons – unlike us when we were students. 'I asked one of them last week what a hospice was, and do you know what he replied? About four and a half litres, sir. Then I asked a female student what she thought of euthanasia. Do you know what she replied? She said she wasn't interested in the problems of the Third World.'

# 6

Last week I admitted a patient to the ward who claimed to have taken eighty of her pills at once. She had cropped hair dyed bright carmine and a devil tattooed on her forehead. I deduced from this that she was not gainfully employed, though I later learnt that she was on a municipal training course in child care.

The next morning she confessed she had taken only eight pills. This was more in keeping with the level of the drug found in her blood.

'I never knew you was going to measure it,' she said with a pout, as if we had done something sneaky and dishonourable.

I asked why she took the pills, suspecting the answer in advance: boyfriend trouble.

'Him and me, we had a row, like.'

What about? I asked.

About her inability to have babies, she said. Her tubes were blocked and the gynaecologists were trying to unblock them, but the boyfriend, who already had three children by another woman, repeatedly taunted her about her failure to conceive.

'He kept going on and on at me, so I either had to take the tablets or kill him,' she said. No other solution presented itself to her.

'Did you take them in front of him?' I asked.

'Yes. It was him what gave me them to take. He said I didn't have the bottle to take them, so I told him I did and he handed them to me one by one and I swallowed them.'

'You realise that in helping you he committed a crime?'

'I don't want to get him into no trouble.'

'I thought you said you wanted to kill him?'

'Yes, one day I will, the filthy little toe-rag.'

'How long have you known him?'

'Three months – since my husband went in prison.'

'What for?'

'Drugs.'

'Now let me get this straight – please correct me if I'm wrong. You propose to have a child by a man whom you have known for three months and whom you regard as a filthy little toe-rag?'

'Yes, that's right.'

'And the gynaecologists are helping you?'

'They haven't done nothing yet.'

'But they're trying?'

'Yes.'

I wrote the history in the notes.

'Here, you're not writing none of this down, are you? If they see that, they won't help me.'

'Oh yes they will,' I said. 'They don't take any notice of things like that.'

Meanwhile, the filthy little toe-rag arrived on the ward. He was young, small and heavily tattooed; he had the expression of a hungry rodent.

As a six-foot-four prison warder had told me only the previous week, small men tend to be wiry and are often awkward to handle; they slip through your fingers like an eel.

The happy couple fell into each other's embrace, kissed and made up – at public expense, naturally. My patient looked blissfully happy, and – radiating joy – came over to thank me for all I had done.

As she and the toe-rag departed the ward arm in arm, I remembered the last line of a famous Chekhov short story: 'Farewell, my treasure.'

# 7

There is only one thing worse than treating working-class patients, and that is treating middle-class ones. The former are inarticulate and ill-informed, the latter articulate and ill-informed. The former read the *Sunday Sport* and believe there is an immortality clinic on the far side of the moon where Hitler is a patient; the latter read the *Sunday Times* and believe that eating pine-kernels wards off Huntington's chorea.

The trouble with middle-class patients is that they ask so many questions. All children go through a phase of asking 'Why?' and before long parents find themselves confronted by the fundamental, if unanswerable, questions of the universe; something similar happens when middle-class patients consult their doctors. When an unanswerable question about a drug is finally reached, patients feel vindicated: it is true, then, that their doctors are poisoning them with drugs of whose effects and mechanism of action they are ignorant.

In these circumstances, it is scarcely surprising that patients turn to herbs and homeopaths. The very word 'herbal' conjures up something soothing, something natural, something healing, an innocent little plant ruffled by the wind on an open moor, perhaps, or a tiny delicate flower blushing by a babbling brook. How could such a thing do any harm, especially compared with the products of the pharmaceutical industry, with its greed for profits, its horrible animal experiments, its river-polluting factories? It is inconceivable.

A lady came to me last week with one of those grave, chronic illnesses which afflict the middle classes, but which are not incompatible with a long and otherwise healthy life and which stubbornly refuse to manifest themselves in such a way as to be detectable by any of the thousands of methods available to modern science. The symptoms of her illness were vague but debilitating: she could no longer summon up the energy to do the thing she did not wish to do, such as vacuum-cleaning and ironing.

An 'alternative' practitioner (whose treatment was additional, by the way, not alternative) had told her she suffered from an infection – not in its vulgar, immediately apparent form, but in its insubstantial, Platonic form – and that she had better take his treatment for a decade or two if she were ever to rid herself of it. His treatment consisted of herbal pills of high efficacy but low toxicity.

By coincidence, I had a patient two days later who, wishing to bring a lover and the world to heel, had taken an overdose of these gentle, natural pills. I called up the local poison information centre, and here is what they told me about the unwanted effects of these pills:

> Acute overdosage is most likely to lead to drowsiness, ataxia and mild hypotension . . . Therapeutic use may cause malaise with the delayed onset of jaundice due to acute hepatitis. The liver enzymes may be raised due to liver damage and intrahepatic obstruction. Ascites and encephalopathy may develop. Jaundice has been reported after taking only three pills, one a day for three days.

Quite nasty, really – just like the products of the pharmaceutical industry, in fact.

'He choked on a placebo.'

# 8

Everyone knows how important the medical profession is. Can one travel more than a few miles on a bus or train without overhearing the words, 'And my doctor said to me . . .'?

Unsurprisingly, then, many doctors conclude that they are personally very significant in the lives of their patients. Alas, they are wrong. I have a friend who devotes his whole life to his patients, who denies them nothing, who will go to almost any lengths to please them even at their most unreasonable.

He is such a nice man that he imagines that behind every complaint there must lie suffering (rather than, say, laziness, ignorance or stupidity), and tries to alleviate it.

He deserves to be loved and respected. Sometimes, when he is unavoidably absent from his surgery, I stand in for him. Naturally, being impatient of human weakness, I worry that I shall not be able to match his high standard of compassion. I needn't worry, however: the first patient of the day convinces me of this.

I press the buzzer and the patient, all eager for the treat, enters trippingly. Rising to greet him or her, I start my standard speech for such an occasion.

'Good morning,' I say. 'My name is Dr Dalrymple and I'm here because Dr S— is away for a few days.'

But before I can finish, the patient interrupts me.

'Only it's my ears, doctor. Them pills what you gave me, they aren't doing no good.'

Is the patient blind? I never gave him or her any pills, and I don't look anything like Dr S—. But the patient has failed to notice: for him or her neither Dr S— nor I are real people, individuals in our own right, but Platonic forms, disembodied pro-

19

viders of prescriptions, sick notes and referral letters to hospital. It doesn't worry me particularly to be a Platonic form, but I feel rather sad on Dr S—'s behalf.

He thinks his patients value his efforts, but in fact he is valued only for his function, as a vacuum cleaner or washing machine is valued.

In the war between doctor and patient – or at least in their struggle for supremacy – doctors are often accused of not treating the whole patient, of regarding him or her as a pathology specimen rather than a sentient being. Yes, but we doctors are only retaliating for the treatment we receive. If you prick us do we not bleed, if you tickle us do we not laugh etc?

One of Dr S—'s patients came to me in a panic because he had just received a computerised letter from the hospital to say that he was going to be operated on next day. He had been to outpatients some time before about his abdominal pain, but this was the first he had heard of an operation.

I phoned the surgeon concerned to ask what exactly was going to be done. He struggled for a time to recall the patient.

'Isn't he the Meckel's diverticulum?' he asked at last.

I turned to the patient.

'Aren't you the Meckel's diverticulum?' I asked.

# 9

Family life is the backbone of the country, which is why it – the country, I mean – is always going to the dogs. Last week, I met a patient who set a new standard of filial impiety: he tried to push his mother into a fish frier. Fortunately, he got only as far as her bouffant hair-do, otherwise the reputation of the family business (fish and chips) might have been ruined beyond redemption.

One swallow doesn't make a summer, of course, but three days later I came across another fine example of family life. I received a call informing me that the head of a family was threatening to buy a gun and shoot his children before shooting himself. I rushed to the house, in the hope that I would arrive before he had completed his purchase.

He was a stocky man, and I noticed at once that he had scratches on his face. These he received in the course of a quarrel with his wife, who was sitting, pale and vengeful, on the sofa opposite.

Not long before, he had tried to set fire to the house and its inhabitants. He sprinkled the walls and the children with lighter fuel and then directed matches at them. He did this because his wife had come home late one evening and he had noticed a mark on her neck. He said it was a love bite from a clandestine lover, but she said it was a bruise from the last time he tried to strangle her. He did this occasionally, his wife explained.

'He strangled me before Christmas,' she said. 'I had Jason in me arms then, and it's bound to affect him, isn't it, doctor?'

Her husband had always had a vile temper.

'Even his mother threw him out,' she said with thin and bloodless lips.

21

'Why was that?' I asked him.

'I belted our Mum.'

Naturally, he had been to prison. Five years ago he had driven a car recklessly and crashed. Two of his friends were killed and his brother paralysed.

He drank too much now, and was possessed by jealousy. He hunted the house for evidence of his wife's infidelity, finding it in fibres and hairs on the floor, and she was now too terrified of incurring his accusations to speak to anyone in her family, let alone strangers.

I asked him whether he had ever considered suicide.

'Yes,' he replied. 'I might hang myself.'

'Or shoot yourself?'

'Yes,' he said. 'But first I'd kill the children. It would be a way of getting back at her.' He pointed venomously at his wife.'

'And have you ever thought you would be doing them a favour?'

'Yes,' he said. 'I would be.'

I looked at Jason who had come to his mother's bony lap. He had a chest condition; his face was thin and vacant. He would grow up illiterate and unemployable, fodder for social workers. For the briefest of moments, I wondered whether the father had a point after all: but no, I thought, that way madness lies.

'She got an injunction.'

# 10

Patients who drink too much are notoriously vague (to put it charitably) about the amount they drink. I have a simple method of eliciting the truth from them: I ask them whether they drink two bottles of Scotch a day. 'Oh no, doctor,' they reply, genuinely horrified. 'Only one.'

These days, when epidemiology has revealed the dangers lurking everywhere, doctors have no choice but to concern themselves with their patients' eating, drinking, smoking, sleeping and working habits. I am so heartily sick of the tepid existence which we doctors are now peddling as the elixir of life that when one of my patients refuses to take my good advice, I want to jump up on my table and give three cheers.

I once practised in a very remote corner of the globe, somewhat lacking in sophisticated medical facilities (other than myself, of course). One day an Englishman appeared, new in the country. No sooner had he arrived than his legs swelled up, and he came to consult me. He was extremely large – what failed dieters call big-boned – and very fat. He lost no time in telling me he was diabetic.

'Do you smoke?' I asked.

'Like a chimney,' he replied.

He was completely unrepentant, so refreshingly different from all those snivelling wheedlers with hang-dog expressions who give you a long story about how they nearly gave up but then their budgerigar died. I got the picture at once.

'And of course, you drink like a fish,' I said.

'Like a fish,' he replied.

'Dieting is out of the question?' I continued, with mounting admiration.

'Completely, I love butter and cream, and meat

with fat on it, and rich sauces.'

'Well,' I said, 'I'm sure you know the risks better than I, so I'm not going to lecture you. But if you invite me to dinner, I shall come.'

That was twelve years ago. His wife was, and is, a magnificent cook. I wish I could say the story had a happy ending, but honesty compels me to relate that recently he had two heart attacks which have laid him low. He can hardly breathe, and now he needs cardiac surgery.

Still, I found his refusal to do the sensible thing heroic in its way, and it gave him a dozen years of untrammelled life. He may yet pull through. I know there are medical fascists around – a former President of the Royal College of Physicians is one – who would make such patients pay for the treatment of their 'self-induced' diseases, but this seems to me to come perilously close to the Erewhonian nightmare, in which youths who bash old ladies over the head will receive treatment, but people with heart attacks will be punished.

In any case, patients know their doctors have feet of clay. Last Monday morning, a man whom I know to be a very heavy drinker consulted me because he was feeling ill. I examined him.

'I can't find anything wrong,' I said. 'It must be the drink.'

'It's all right, doctor,' he said. 'I'll come back when you're sober.'

# 11

I dread the arrival of the hospital postman. He always brings large manila envelopes containing long circulars from the bureaucrats who pullulate in the halls of the Health Service like generals in a South American army. Everyone seems to be a director of something or other these days (liaison services, resource management, project development, manpower co-ordination), and to suffer from graphomania to boot.

As one might have expected from the constipated titles of the new Health Service aristocracy, the literary quality of these circulars leaves something to be desired. Generally, I throw them away unread. I suppose I should keep them for scrap, but even if I were going to rewrite *Encyclopaedia Britannica* every year, I should not need so much paper. Sometimes I declaim a portion of a circular to my secretary, who goes weak with laughter, not at my imitation of Donald Wolfit but at the grammar.

Last week I received a circular entitled *Joint Care Planning to J.C.C.G.P.T. by Task Group for C.M.H.T.'s.* It arrived with a small slip of paper, saying that it was a slightly amended version of the original draft, which should now be destroyed. Too late! I had destroyed it already.

For a reason which I now cannot recall, I opened this twenty-page circular, of which someone was evidently very proud because it came in its own black folder. My eye fell on a section entitled *Service Sensitivity to Particular Groups*. Paraphrase will not do it justice, so I must quote *in extenso*.

> Equal opportunities are not easily achieved. To have a policy and a strategy are insufficient. There has to be an internalisation of its fundamental philosophy which does not mean 'everyone is equal. I treat

people the same whatever'. It is, however, to do with the differences between people, the uniqueness of each person. In terms of service delivery it is within CMHT's that greater expression should be able to be given to the philosophy of equal opportunities in that by focusing on a given area with the benefit of a multi skill group together with users of the service a very clear strategy can be drawn up within the operation policy of each team that will lead not to a bland overall response to need but one that is tailored to and by the individual and community. In recruitment, selection and retention of staff, statutory and voluntary organisations need to continue to address the issue of achieving a shared understanding of what equal opportunities actually means and how it is to be put into practice.

Insofar as this passage means anything – beyond its menacingly imperative tone – it means that you can't expect blacks to be the equal of whites, so they must be given jobs which, strictly speaking, they don't really deserve.

Some opportunities are more equal than others.

I often flee from the approach of the hospital postman and take refuge in the medical library. Last week, seeking temporary asylum there, I happened on the *British Journal of Psychiatry*. It fell open at a paper entitled *Age, Transvestism, Bondage and Concurrent Paraphilic Activities in 117 Fatal Cases of Autoerotic Asphyxia*.

'She started it – she smacked me
on the bottom.'

# 12

To mock the bourgeois virtues is, of course, a bourgeois privilege and pastime, and we do it not because the virtues are not virtuous, but to demonstrate to the world our superior intellect. But there is something heroic about the struggle of poor people to attain respectability, and failure to appreciate this heroism demonstrates the cruelty and lack of imagination of many self-appointedly superior intellects.

Last week a middle-aged West Indian lady of ample proportions consulted me. She wore a frock of many frills, and upon her head perched an elaborate hat complete with veil and exotic feathers, which it lifted my heart to see. It did not take long to discover that her symptoms were out of proportion to her actual illness.

She came to this country with her husband more than thirty years ago, and both of them had worked hard ever since. They had bought their house – a small thing, perhaps, but their own. They had two sons, the beginning of their troubles.

The first had left school at the age of sixteen, despite the pleas of his parents to continue his education. On leaving school, he settled for a life of sloth, rising at one in the afternoon, and going to bed at four in the morning. On the insistence of his father, he eventually found a job as an apprentice mechanic, but gave it up after a month, first because it interfered with his nocturnal social life, and second because he said that the employer was making money out of him. Elementary social justice demanded that he lived for evermore on social security: anything else would have been exploitation.

The second son stayed on at school and went to college to study law. After a year, however, he gave up his studies because he said he could not condone a system that sent offenders to gaol. He began to mix with what his mother described as 'bad company' – ganja smokers and the like. Before long, he was involved in a robbery and was sentenced to two years of gaol.

At this point, my patient began to cry. Visiting her son in gaol every two weeks had been a slow and agonising torture for her. Her husband had become embittered and his tirades against what he called his layabout sons poisoned the home atmosphere yet further. Only her membership of the Pentecostal Church, which she attended four times a week, sustained her. Recently, for the first time, she had been granted the gift of tongues, and it had made her happy.

'We try to lead a clean life, doctor,' she said. 'How can I put it? We are in the world, but not of the world.'

How does such a woman come to have two self-righteously lazy and aggressively worthless sons? How has her dream of thirty years ago been turned into this nightmare? I do not have the whole explanation, but I suspect that those who teach that employment is exploitation, that law is injustice, and that racial prejudice is so ubiquitous and all-pervading as to render personal effort superfluous, have much to answer for.

# 13

Many of my patients are like Wagner: they have their good moments but their bad quarters of an hour. I have a patient whose torrential loquacity leaves my head spinning, but who occasionally says something worth hearing, in much the same way as a monkey at a typewriter must (according to the arguments advanced in *Watchtower* and *Awake*) eventually produce Shakespeare. I give my patient an appointment to see me once a month, not because I am vain enough to suppose I shall cure him, but because he would otherwise plague me every day.

He is in many ways a most unfortunate man. Physically slight, he lives in an area of the city where life is red in tooth and claw. Two youths once up-ended him as he came out of the post office and shook the sickness benefit out of him, as I used to shake the pennies out of my brother's piggy bank when I was a delinquent child.

Last week I signed his sickness certificate for a further year. How time flies! It seems but yesterday that I signed his last twelve-month guarantee of medical unfitness for work. (Round here, the relationship between ill health and sickness benefits is what I dare say a great Marxist thinker like E. J. Hobsbawm would call *dialectical*.) The only problem with the certificate was that it demanded a diagnosis: eventually, I struck on *congenital nervous debility*.

My patient looked at what I had written and, far from being distressed by it, asked me whether I couldn't, perhaps, give him a certificate for life, as this would save time in the long run. I couldn't, I said, and we passed on to other problems.

'It's my wife, doctor,' he said. 'She doesn't understand my mental requirement for sex.'

31

This unfortunate misunderstanding had led to a liaison with Pam, a sixty-year-old widow who lived nearby. 'I try to stop myself, doctor, but I just can't. She's a temptress, that's what she is, a temptress.'

As it happens, I know Pam quite well: she is also a patient of mine. Her most prominent features are her false teeth and her curlers. It is difficult to imagine her as Cleopatra to his Antony.

'Why do I do it, doctor? Can't you give me a psychoanalysis or something?'

Evidently he conceived of psychoanalysis as a kind of suppository, taken once and for all.

'I'm afraid not,' I said, looking at my watch.

'What about hypnosis, then?' he asked. 'Can't you hypnotise me to be a better person?'

How often have I heard such requests! Husbands who want to stop beating their wives, divorced women who want to stop remarrying violent layabouts, drunkards who want to be calm.

They don't really want to change, of course, any more than they believe I can change them. Weakness and vice are like symptoms: one soon grows attached to them.

'I'm afraid I can't make you better than you are,' I said.

'That's a pity, doctor,' said my patient. 'When's my next appointment, then?

'I'm not having it, Mr Robinson - you're a hypochondriac.'

# 14

Every week I receive through the post several invitations to medical conferences, meetings, seminars and colloquia. Someone somewhere is under the mistaken impression that I have difficulty filling my time. Despite my busy schedule, however, one such invitation caught my attention last week: it was to something called a Doctors' Liberation Workshop. The fee was £30, which included lunch and caffeine-free drinks.

The workshop was organised and led by a doctor who described herself as 'interested in liberation issues', and who also ran a parents' liberation group. Presumably, while not 'setting up ongoing listening partnerships', the group fire-bombs schools. Needless to say, I nearly signed up for the workshop: and in the space reserved in the registration form for 'special needs', I nearly wrote 'caffeine'.

I'm all in favour of doctors' liberation, of course, of 'freeing ourselves from the feelings that stop us thinking clearly and creatively about our work' and 'looking at specific aspects of being a doctor which we commonly struggle with' – especially after what happened last Tuesday.

The first overdose patient of the day was a lady with a DSH (a drunken swine of a husband). When drunk, he used regularly to beat her, preferably in front of the children, and after several years of this behaviour, she had had enough. The only way out was death.

She took the pills with the DSH looking on. 'Go on,' he said, 'take as many as you like. Take more, kill yourself, see if I care.'

He went to the bathroom to fetch more pills and gave them to her. When she had finished them, he decided it was time to 'make love'. Only afterwards did he call an ambulance.

Two hours after the first, the next overdose patient arrived. She had taken her pills in the park, and an ambulance was called only when a passer-by noticed her vomiting into the flower beds.

The patient, who was thirty-four years old, had been married for fifteen years. Her husband was the boy next door; she had never known anyone else. The romance had departed from her life a long time ago, and her husband, who still loved her, drove her mad by his taciturn kindness.

'I've tried to quarrel with him for years, doctor,' she said, 'but he's just too placid. If I criticise him, he agrees with me and says he'll try to reform. I've even tried burning his dinner four nights in a row, but all he does is thank me and say that it's very nice.'

She had a religious upbringing, and so regarded marriage as sacred and indissoluble; this only added to her burden of guilt.

'I've fallen out of love with him, doctor,' she said. 'It's terrible to have to live with a man you don't love any more. The worst thing is, he's done nothing wrong to make me fall out of love with him. He's still the same quiet, decent man I married. This may sound silly to you, but the thing I really can't stand about him is that he's so nice.' She laughed, and then burst into tears.

So drunken swinishness and stoic decency came to the same thing in the end; or nearly the same. The lady whose husband beat her regularly returned to him; the lady whose husband never raised his voice against her fled the matrimonial home and is suing for divorce.

# 15

Last week I went to Meadowlea, where so many of our vilest murderers are held (the more arcadian or botanical the name of a prison, the worse its inmates).

Of course, I arrived at an inconvenient moment: the murderers were having their after-lunch nap, and couldn't be disturbed.

I was shown into a waiting room where the only reading matter was a Prison Officers' Association pamphlet denouncing the Government's plans to privatise the prison service. As luck would have it, I had Tolstoy's *The Kreutzer Sonata* with me, so I did not mind waiting while the prison officers had their afternoon nap as well.

Eventually, the murderer whom I was to examine was brought to me. He was very polite, I must say; he was soft-spoken and did not sit until I invited him to do so. It was difficult to imagine him bashing his wife's head with a brick.

The problem was that he couldn't remember having done so. His was one of those and-the-next-thing-I-knew-doctor-she-wasn't-breathing-any-more type of murders.

My task was to determine whether his loss of memory was caused by a brain tumour, a dysfunction of his glands, or moral depravity.

I recalled a passage from *The Kreutzer Sonata*:

When people say they don't remember what they do in a fit of fury, it is rubbish, falsehood. I remember everything, and did not for a moment lose my memory ... I felt, and remember, the momentary resistance of her corset and of something else, and then the plunging of the dagger into something soft ... I remembered that for an instant before the action I had a terrible consciousness that I was killing, had killed a

36

defenceless woman, my wife. I remember the horror
of that consciousness . . . and even dimly remember
that, having plunged the dagger in, I pulled it out
immediately, trying to remedy what had been done.

Of course, I shouldn't let a mere fiction such as
Tolstoy's interfere with my judgment in an individual
case. Nevertheless, I cannot help but notice that the
number of criminals claiming medical explanations
for their misdeeds is inexorably rising.

This is good for my income, of course, but bad for
taxpayers (who fund, through Legal Aid, my expert
opinions).

A lady consulted me last week who had been
caught embezzling the treasury of the local council
for which she worked. £4,000 had gone missing over
the last few years, and she was very distressed about it.
She was accompanied into my office by her husband,
a ferret-faced man who spoke on her behalf while she
sobbed into a paper handkerchief.

'She didn't do it for herself, doctor,' he said. 'She
never bought nothing for herself with the money, only
for the children.'

She sobbed convulsively, out of compassion for
herself.

'Why did she do it, doctor?' asked her husband.
'I mean, there must be a reason. She's never done
anything like it before.'

'She wanted the money, I suppose,' I thought,
but it came out, 'I haven't a clue.'

The husband paled with anger. He raised his wife
by the elbow and pointed her towards the door,

'Come on, Marge,' he said. 'We're going. This
is useless.'

When they reached the door, he turned to me.
'Typical NHS,' he snarled.

'Please Doctor - put me out of
your misery.'

# 16

I read a book not long ago which maintained that the essential difference between Man and the animals was that Man had a concept of the future, which allowed him to foresee and plan ahead. I can only remark that the author of this book must have confined his observations to a very restricted social circle indeed.

Last week I arrived on the ward to find a young woman in bed with tears and smudged make-up running down her pale cheeks. Her hair was dyed blonde, with dark roots, and by means of the hair-dresser's art it had been induced to stick out of the side of her head in straggly and crinkly strands, like a feather from a hat. Her jaw was broken.

I surmised at a glance that her story was dismal, and so it proved. Aged seventeen, she was the un-married mother of two children by the man who had just broken her jaw. She had left him, she said, a few months before, when she decided to move from one area of the city to another and he had refused to follow her. He had punched her in the face while on a visit to what she called 'the babby'.

She said she didn't know what to do, for she lived in terror of him. I suggested, naïvely as it transpired, that she take out an injunction against him.

'I've already got one of those,' she said. 'But it's no use.'

She had called the police three times when her ex-boyfriend broke the terms of the injunction, but the police had done nothing. I was exasperated by this inactivity of the police: nowadays they seem to do nothing even when a crime is committed in front of their noses. Then again, perhaps the leniency of the courts is to blame for the police's inertia.

'And how many times has your ex-boyfriend broken the injunction against him?' I asked.

'About seventy,' she said.

'And how does he get in?' I asked.

'He pushes the door when I open it.'

'Why do you open it to him?'

'I don't know it's him.'

'But you must suspect by now that it might be him. Don't you ask?'

'No.'

'Don't you have a chain on your front door?'

'Yes.'

'Don't you use it?'

'No.'

'Why not?'

'I forget.'

I began to see the method in the police's inertia. If they charged the swine, she would eventually refuse to testify against him. At the age of seventeen, with two children, she needed him even as he smashed her in the face. He would never be called to account for his actions.

In the next bed was a fifteen-year-old girl with abdominal pain. She too was crying. I looked into her vacant, ruminant eyes and I knew she was pregnant. So it turned out to be.

Of course, her boyfriend had deserted her. She'd known him for ages (three months) and had become pregnant deliberately because he'd threatened to leave her. As far as she was concerned, life without Jason wasn't worth living.

I had a book with me, *The Anatomy of the Nuremberg Trials* by Telford Taylor, and asked her to read the title. She could progress no further than the first syllable of the second word.

'What are your interests?' I asked.

'I don't have none,' she replied, after a long pause for thought.

'And how do you see your future?' I asked.

She shook her head.

'I haven't thought about it.'

40

# 17

It is a well-known fact that one of the best pre-
servatives against ill health is self-employment. The
self-employed cannot afford to be ill, while those in
the employ of others cannot afford (it often seems) to
be entirely well. A friend of mine once ran a business in
which he tried to employ young British school leavers.
The attempt very nearly bankrupted him. As one of his
young employees said to him when upbraided about
his continual absences from work, 'But I'm *entitled* to
two days sick a week.'

The epidemiological distinction between self-employment and employ by others receives startling
confirmation in Her Majesty's prisons. Every prisoner
has to be medically examined within twenty-four
hours of being received into custody, and the doctor
has not only to screen for any illnesses, but allocate a
work category. The interview is often rather sticky.

'Have you seen your doctor recently?'

'I can't remember.'

'Well, have a try.'

'I think it might have been this morning.'

'Either it was this morning or it wasn't.'

'I can't remember.'

'Have another try.'

'It was this morning.'

'And why did you go to see him?'

'Depression.'

'What were you depressed about?'

'I can't remember.'

'It wasn't all that long ago.'

'My court case.'

Last week, one of the prisoners – a burglar –
tried to hang himself in police custody because his
wife had decided to leave him.

'She says she's fed up with me being arrested all the time.'

'Are you going to go straight, then?' I asked.

'I'm trying,' he said. 'This is my first offence since Christmas.'

'Do you offend often?'

'Not as often as I used to. I'm cutting it down gradually, doctor.'

'Like smoking,' I said.

It's amazing how many criminals have had serious road accidents — almost all of them, in fact. Most have artificial bits of skulls and pins and plates in their legs, and all of them without exception have healed lacerations of their wrists, from when they 'fell through a window', in their eagerness no doubt to reach the video or stereo set. Quite a few have a tattoo round their nipples saying 'Made in England', but I suppose that is quite another matter.

Usually, though, the allocation of a work category poses no problems. The majority of prisoners, pins and plates notwithstanding, are category IA. The main problem in categorisation is those who appear in prison with a walking stick.

'It's the arthuritis, doctor,' they say. 'I've had it for years. It really plays me up.'

'Are you taking any medicine for it?' I ask.

'Yes, doctor, the little white ones.'

'I don't suppose you can remember what they're called?'

'No, doctor, I'm sorry.'

'And how bad is it, the arthuritis?'

'It's terrible, doctor. I can't climb no stairs. Can you locate me flat, please doctor?'

*Locate flat* means that the prisoner lives on the ground floor and is not required to climb stairs to fetch his food or go to work.

'And what are you in prison for?'

42

'Burglary, doctor.'
'Then I suppose that you must specialise in ground-floor flats and bungalows.'

'You say I drink too much -
what about the second opinion?'

# 18

Last week, I was quietly exercising the inalienable right of every doctor to read the newspaper in his consulting room while his patients queue up outside waiting to see him, when the telephone rang. I answered it with bad grace because I was thoroughly absorbed at the time in a story about a man in Bradford who, though he had no medical training, had successfully posed as a general practitioner for thirty years without detection either by patients or by colleagues. I must say the prosecution seemed to have got its priorities right: it was outraged more by the money gained under false pretences by the pseudo-doctor than by any damage he might have done to his pseudo-patients.

'Doctor, come quick,' said the distracted female voice on the telephone. 'He's trying to kill her.'

Who was he? Who was she? I did not recognise the voice, so I enquired.

'Only there's guns in the house and he's gone mad.'

Eventually, I managed to extract the madman's name and address from the lady, who proved to be his daughter. The police had been called the night before but had taken the view that if a man wants to kill his wife it is his own affair. Presumably they, the police, would be rather more interested after the event.

I set out at once – or nearly at once, after I finished my coffee to be precise. It was some consolation to me that my patients would now have to wait a little longer for me (I could just hear them say 'Dr Dalrymple's such a busy man, always on the go') as a result of the emergency call to forestall murder.

My journey took me through one of the more salubrious quarters of my stamping ground, where housewives lead semi-detached lives in semi-detached houses. Even here, the litter is not swept from the streets: the council is too busy running resource centres for lesbians from ethnic minorities to bother with mere trifles like litter.

As I approached the address of the homicidal maniac, I suddenly remembered the guns. Would *The Spectator* print an obituary of me if my patient shot me instead of his wife? Looking around at the urban desolation, death suddenly seemed quite attractive. Then I recalled a sentence from an obituary of a physician in the *Lancet* some years ago:

> Though not immediately likeable, those who knew
> him well detected many sterling qualities.

And I resolved to live.

The house was in a road called The Twiggs, its vaguely rural connotations giving some intimation of its council estate squalor. The people in a Lowry painting are more like celebrants of the Rio carnival than they are like the residents of The Twiggs. But I was treated as a Daniel come to judgment.

On the wall was an old photograph of Churchill. The 'guns' were brass knick-knacks over the mantelpiece. The homicidal maniac was extremely polite (though hallucinating) and agreed at once to go to hospital. His wife, who was diabetic and had had a stroke, was very relieved.

Did I need a medical degree to deal with this kind of thing, or only an air of authority? Was, then, the pseudo-doctor of Bradford such a fantastical rogue after all?

# 19

I was called to the casualty department last week. A fifteen-year-old boy had taken an overdose and was being obstreperous – from habit, I hasten to add, not from the toxic effects of the drug he had taken. Clearly, something in his life was unsatisfactory, and I resolved to find out what it was. I adopted my very best compassionate tone of voice.

'Fuck off,' said the little bastard (and he was a bastard too, as are most of the children round here).

Choking down my anger, I thought what to do next. The obvious thing was to telephone his mother. I could hear a medley of reggae music and screaming baby in the background when the receiver was lifted.

'Hello. My name is Dr Dalrymple and I'm calling from the general hospital. Could I speak to Mrs R—, please?'

'Yes.'

There was a prolonged pause.

'Is Mrs R— there?' I asked.

'I'm Mrs R—,' replied the same voice.

'Could you tell me a little about Darren?' I asked.

She certainly could. All children called Darren, Wayne, Jason, Tracy, Kirsty or Kylie are destined for misery and several unsuccessful attempts at suicide.

'Where shall I begin? He was expelled from school when he was seven.'

'What did he do?' I asked.

'He beat up the teacher.'

I know that children mature early these days, but even so, this seemed an astonishingly precocious feat.

'What happened then?' I asked.

'He was put in a special school,' she said.

'What kind of special school?'

'You know, where all the kids had something wrong with them, like asthma or brittle bones.'

That sounded like social services all right: brittle bones and uncontrollable violence in the same institution. Anything less would be unwarranted discrimination.

The special school failed to make much of an impact on Darren, either educationally or behaviourally. He continued to beat people up from time to time; as his mother put it, 'He's always been awkward, like, but he's never committed a crime.'

His father, separated from his mother when he was born, would have nothing to do with him: 'His father don't want to know. He had him for a week once and that was enough.'

His mother's present lover, Angel, had tried a few times to discipline him.

'But that child is not a small child, he's a good-sized boy,' his mother said. 'He really deserves a good backsiding, though. Once he was mouthing me off and I cut his arm with a broken bottle to relieve the tension out of my head. His stepdad slapped him one and Darren said, "I can have you up for assault." '

It seemed to me that we couldn't sort things out over the telephone. The first thing to do was to change his name from Darren to Clive. I asked the mother to come to the hospital. Meanwhile, Darren had a well-earned sleep.

His mother arrived. It was clear she had been about sixteen when Darren was born. 'I just can't handle him no more,' she said.

I shook Darren awake.

'Darren,' I said. 'Your mother's here.'

'Fuck off,' he said.

# 20

One of the few lessons I have learnt as a doctor is that, life being what it is, things turn out badly in the end. I don't just mean death, which is bad enough, of course; I mean, rather, that the interval between birth and death is a compendium, a veritable bestiary, of disasters.

Take maternal love, for example. Those who never had it say that it was the lack of it which made them rob post-offices and go to prison. Those, on the other hand, who did have it say that it smothered them, made them complacent and sapped them of ambition, which is why they are still in the same intolerably tedious dead-end jobs.

When I discussed this insoluble problem with a French doctor friend of mine, she quoted a passage from a novel by Romain Gary, to the effect that those who knew maternal love in childhood are bound to be disappointed later in life, which can never fulfil its early promise. All human relationships after mother-love are ruined by 'the poison of comparison'.

It is just the same with religion. Those who have no belief are adrift in a vast and meaningless universe, without moral bearings. But those who believe are tormented by their inevitable failure to live according to their precepts.

A respectable middle-aged lady who was taking antidepressant tablets consulted me last week about her religious torment. She belonged to one of those churches where people speak in tongues and call one another brother and sister. The peculiarity of her sect was that it believed in and prescribed 'the Holy Kiss': after each service, everyone kissed everyone else, not erotically, of course, but as a gesture of universal, all-encompassing love.

49

Unhappily for my patient, there was in the congregation a lesbian who lingered somewhat over the Holy Kiss. My patient asked her to desist, but to no effect. She asked her again the following week, also to no effect. The third time she slapped her face in full view of the rest of the congregation, which, unaware of what had gone before, was deeply shocked by this outbreak of unsisterly behaviour.

The church warned her that any repetition would result in expulsion (to say nothing of eternal flames). But my patient still felt bitter and angry about the lesbian, and her hostile feelings troubled her conscience.

She said that her faith enjoined her always to turn the other cheek and love those who wronged her as herself, but she found that in this case it was simply impossible. Furthermore, it was a tenet of her religion that failure to achieve complete serenity was a sign of insufficient faith.

I asked her whether, perhaps, she was not being a little hard on herself. Were the other members of the congregation stainless and immaculate?

'We are not supposed to judge ourselves by others, doctor,' she said. 'We are supposed to become Christ-like.'

'Yes, but . . .' I began to object.

'What do I have without my faith, doctor? Nothing.'

It was true: her life heretofore had been utterly wretched, and her faith had only recently redeemed it.

'Have you been to see your pastor about this?' I asked.

'Yes.'

'And what does he say?'

'He says I should keep on taking the tablets.'

# 21

From time to time, I make house-calls under the protection of the police. This is because some of my patients are inclined to violence and I have no thirst for martyrdom. No matter how deluded and paranoid people are, they are usually able to refrain from attacking several policemen, each of whom is over six feet tall.

Last week, one of my patients, a young West Indian, held a knife to his poor, blameless mother's throat, apparently in the belief that she was the Whore of Babylon. He knew this to be the case because the voices told him so. His mother was terrified of him, for he had acted thus before and, like many paranoids in our slums, he was not only physically strong but trained in martial arts. He was now holed up in his flat, which we had a magistrate's warrant to enter.

His flat was in one of those cheerless tower blocks which, to adapt very slightly Le Corbusier's remark with regard to houses, are machines for going insane in. The illuminated name sign of the block on the fourth-floor wall had been smashed by conscientious vandals, and the megawatt thump of two lots of reggae music ran through the walls like vibrations through a tuning fork. The police are as welcome in such tower blocks as bubonic plague in seventeenth-century London.

'Open up, Steven,' said one of the two policemen who came with me, speaking through the letter-box. 'We want to talk to you.'

A loud stream of what is known technically as *verbal* followed, and I caught a glimpse of the blade of a knife through the letter-box as the policeman withdrew his head with some alacrity.

'I think we need reinforcements,' he said wisely,

and radioed for them.

Before long, six more policemen arrived, two with riot shields. Unfortunately, they were not the only ones to arrive on the scene at the time: two young West Indian men, one a leader and the other a follower, arrived from several floors above to join in and add to the fun.

'What are all these honkies doing here?' asked the leader rhetorically.

'Clear off,' said one of the policemen. 'Can't you see we're busy?'

'Don't open the door, man,' shouted the leader to the mad mother-stabber in the flat. 'They've got shields and truncheons.'

'If you don't clear off,' said the policeman, 'we'll arrest you for obstruction.'

'It's my right to be here, I live here,' said the leader. 'Don't open up, man,' he shouted again.

I approached him.

'Look,' I said, 'this man is dangerous, he's ill and we're trying to take him to hospital, so please go away.'

'Don't give me that fucking shit,' he said. 'Don't open up, man, there's too many of them.'

'One last time, go away or we'll arrest you,' said a policeman.

'We live here, so it's our right to know what's going on. Why don't you leave this brother alone?'

About ten seconds later, the pair of them were under arrest and were hauled out to a police van. They will fondly nurture the injustice done them for the rest of their lives, to justify their antisocial behaviour.

It wasn't exactly mother's day in the area. That same afternoon, I visited another young West Indian who had just head-butted his mother in the belief that she was concealing the keys to his palace from him.

52

'I've got rights,' he said, and slammed the door.
Mothers, of course, have no rights.

# 22

I cannot quite make up my mind which is worse, family life or the lack of it. Suffice it to say that both are dreadful, which proves, I suppose, that life is what pessimists have always taken it for, namely a disagreeable interlude between lengthy periods of oblivion.

I arrived on the ward one day last week to find two nineteen-year-olds lying in adjacent beds. One had tried to poison herself with bleach, the other (a man) with insecticide. Both had failed, though not without causing their medical attendants some anxiety on their behalf. The clinical notes of the young woman commenced with the memorable words 'Overdose of bleach', raising the interesting medical question as to the correct therapeutic dose of bleach.

The young man had recently gone to live with his father for the first time in his life and had not found the experience encouraging. His father was simultaneously pietistic and amoral, his whim was law, and the young man rebelled against him. The father soon resorted to violence and the young man to insecticide.

His upbringing had been conventional – conventional, that is, for this small corner of the world. He had known no stability in childhood, not even the stability of misery. He had been pushed from one unwilling relative to another.

'When you're young, like,' he explained, 'you don't live with your parents.'

I suppose I must have looked surprised by his statement, for he went on to explain himself further.

'You live with your sisters – your half-sisters, you know, different dads, same mum, like – that's the way we do it.'

He spoke as if describing an ancient and honourable custom, yet what a wealth of unhappiness, neglect and cruelty his words implied! Eventually, he had run out of half-sisters – different dads, same mum – with whom he might stay, and was sent to a children's home, which he tried to burn down. There followed the usual cycle of juvenile crime until one day he realised, almost as a religious conversion, that he was responsible for his own actions. By then, he had been released from the children's home and was living with his mother. She, however, died, and he went to live with his father; and now the overdose of weedkiller had left him permanently impaired neurologically.

The young woman in the next bed came from a close-knit Sikh family. They had long wanted to arrange a marriage for her, but she had fallen in love with a man and secretly married him. He was a Sikh, but of lower caste than she. Her parents found a man in India whom they considered a suitable match for her, and took her there to meet him, where eventually she confessed that she was already married.

She was brought back to England, where she was locked up and beaten by her father and uncles until such time as she agreed to repudiate her shameful alliance with the man of lower caste, but she managed to escape and reach her husband. Finding out their whereabouts, however, her family threatened to kill the husband and had once attacked him in the street. A life sentence for murder was, apparently, a small price to pay for restoring family honour in the eyes of the neighbours. And now husband and wife were obliged to live as hermits, never leaving the dingy hostel which was their only refuge.

In misery's house are many mansions.

# 23

When I was a very young man I thought I understood people. All human conduct was attributable in the last analysis to one or two simple motives, whose workings it required only a certain clear-sightedness (which fortunately I possessed) to perceive.

Now that I have had a little more experience of people, I am convinced that I do not understand them at all. Oddly enough, the less I understand them, the more confidence they seem to place in me: and not a few treat me as an oracle. Some even go so far as to follow my instructions, occasionally with unintended consequences. For example, I once prescribed tablets for a man to take every eight hours. He returned a month later in a state of exhaustion verging on collapse.

The man had consulted me at eleven o'clock in the morning, and I told him to start taking the tablets immediately. Ever since then, he had taken them at eleven in the morning, seven in the evening and again at three in the morning, setting his alarm to wake him at that wretched hour. I had ruined his life utterly, but he had kept on taking the tablets and I was rather flattered by his fidelity to the letter of my law.

Strangely enough, prisoners expect me to know everything, especially why they do what they do. An old lag, a recidivist burglar in his sixties, came to my room in the prison last week and asked whether I had five minutes to talk to him.

'Yes,' I replied.

'Good,' he said, sitting himself down opposite me. 'I've wanted to talk to you for a long time. What I want to know, doctor, is why I keep breaking into people's houses.'

'Greed and laziness, I should expect,' I replied.

He looked a little startled.

'What?' he said.

'You want things but can't be bothered to work for them, so you steal them instead.'

'So it hasn't got nothing to do with my unhappy childhood, then?'

'No, absolutely nothing.'

He mused for a moment, pondering these new and exotic ideas. Then, somewhat in a tone of nostalgic regret, he said, 'But I had a job once, doctor.'

As an attempt to prove that he was not lazy, I found his reminiscence unimpressive. 'And what happened to it?'

'It didn't last. I couldn't do it.'

'Why not?'

'I'm a night bird, doctor, and I couldn't get up of a morning.'

'And so you returned to burglary.'

'Yes. But I only stole from them what could afford it.'

'I expect they had more to steal,' I said.

The old lag rose from the seat.

'Thank you, doctor. I'm glad I've seen you.'

'Don't mention it,' I replied.

Next day, back in the hospital, I spoke to a man just before his discharge who looked like a professional hooligan: shaved head, ring through his nose, a skull tattooed on his forearm.

'What are you going to do when you leave hospital?' I asked.

'I don't know,' he said. 'You're the expert.'

'I'm afraid we've left a
swab requisition form inside you.'

# 24

It is a truth universally acknowledged that something must be done about it. And it follows that if something must be done, it can be done.

Since activity is as good as action, the first thing to do is to form a committee. The purpose of this committee is to assure the Health Authority that it can assure the Ministry that it can assure the Minister that he can assure the Government that it can assure the Opposition that something is indeed being done. The ideal committee should have at least the following members: a hospital consultant, a specialist in public health, a policeman, a clergyman, an occupational therapist, a probation officer, a social worker, a local councillor, a physiotherapist, a representative of the voluntary agencies, a JP and a prominent local businessman. This will ensure that the committee cannot meet more than once every four months, and then only after a long list of apologies for absence.

The subject of the committee's deliberations should be vague but important: alcohol is a good example. As everyone is aware, alcohol is responsible for accidents, murder, suicide, cirrhosis, cancer, heart disease, stroke, divorce, crime and ruination, as well as 95 per cent of the enjoyment at social occasions and a considerable, if lesser, proportion of government revenue. It is therefore a perfect candidate for the inaction-through-activity strategy, and indeed every regional health authority now has a Regional Alcohol Co-ordinating Advisory Committee to stem the tide of alcoholic over-indulgence and to act as a government sop to zealots for whom a long and healthy life is necessarily a happy one.

I found myself temporarily co-opted on to one of

these committees a little while ago. Every few months we listen to a lugubrious detective-inspector reading out the drunken offence statistics since our last meeting, usually followed by an account of a Particularly Horrible and Brutal Murder Committed While Under the Influence. We tut-tut with deep feeling, and even shake our heads.

Everything on the committee was proceeding smoothly and serenely when the health authority suddenly gave us £20,000 to spend. This was rather more than could decently be expended on our sandwiches, and the committee's chairperson (it would be invidious to mention her sex) panicked. There was nothing for it but to carry out a survey.

But what did we want to find out? Nothing sprang to mind. We decided to call in a firm of consultants. Their services would cost £12,000 and a part-time secretary would ensure that we overspent slightly, a sure sign of our diligence. The money will have been spent, something will have been done, and the consultants' report will be at least twenty pages long.

# 25

There is a method known to psychologists as *paradoxical intention*, by means of which patients bring about a desired end by striving for its opposite. Thus, insomniacs are instructed to apply all their will-power to staying awake at night, and to pinch their thighs if they feel themselves sinking into the arms of Morpheus (to turn poetic for once).

How typical of Man that he should aim at one thing and achieve another! That is why I have never really believed in health education, especially when it is directed at the young, who are generally even more perverse than their parents. Told not to smoke, they will at once light up. I don't suppose I should ever have taken marijuana, amphetamines or cocaine had they received the seal of *Good Housekeeping*.

When the Government began to spend our hard-earned money on Aids education, therefore, I knew at once (on general principles) that its campaign would be at best redundant and at worst harmful, to say nothing of its completely predictable mendacity. Of course, there are those who will maintain that the non-occurrence of a heterosexual epidemic of Aids, so long foreseen by experts from the slough of Epidemiological Despond, is sufficient proof of the necessity and effectiveness of the campaign, and that now is not the moment to drop our guard (or expenditure); but such people may safely be ignored. Their jobs depend upon a permanent effervescence of publicly funded panic.

No doubt the motives behind some of the untruths which we were told in the course of the campaign, for example that 'Aids is not prejudiced', were honourable. The epidemic was sometimes likened in severity to the Black Death, and, as everyone knows, popular responses to epidemics of plague in mediaeval and early modern Europe were not always fully rational. Scapegoats were found, and in those countries which had not already expelled them the Jews were accused of poisoning the wells. It was probably felt that our population, being even worse educated than it was in 1348, might respond discreditably to the idea that Aids was a disease of certain groups, and indulge in pogroms against them. It was to avoid such behaviour that the truth was concealed by slick advertisers' slogans.

While I have every respect for the ability of the public to grasp the wrong end of the stick, and to worry itself to distraction over small and distant risks while disregarding large and near ones, I feel that honesty would have been a better policy on the whole (though I acknowledge that such a policy doesn't come naturally to any government). The problem with disseminating untruths is that they will be eventually found out, further destroying belief in legitimate authority and inducing a cynical nihilism.

The Government has spent more than £800 million on the containment of Aids through health education, and it appears that Aids has been more or less contained, *ergo* (some will say) the money was well-spent. Certainly the army of careworkers, co-ordinators, project leaders, outreach workers, counsellors and others – larger than the legions of the afflicted – which the disease has spawned have enjoyed seven fat years and helped reduce the numbers of the unemployed.

The question I ask myself, and the real mystery of the epidemic, is where did they all come from, and what did they do before there was Aids?

# 26

One morning last week, I was woken by the telephone. It was three o'clock and I groaned like someone coming round from an anaesthetic.

'It's the prison here, doctor. I'm the night sister. Sorry to bother you at this hour, but L519726 Jones has just swallowed a safety-pin.'

'Open or closed?' I mumbled.

'I'm sorry doctor, what did you say?'

'Was the safety-pin open or closed?'

'I don't know, doctor. I'll go and ask.'

Vague and indistinct noises emanated from the telephone receiver, followed some time later by approaching footsteps.

'He says it was open, doctor.'

'Why did he do it?' I asked.

'I don't know, doctor. I'll go and ask.'

There were the same indistinct noises and approaching footsteps.

'He says it was boredom.'

Boredom? Good God, what do they expect in prison, an all-night cabaret?

'Send him to casualty,' I said, and rolled over.

Next morning, I met him in the prison hospital. He looked fresher than I. An X-ray had revealed that it had been a false alarm, the safety-pin was closed, and eventually he would pass it *per rectum*.

'It must have closed itself on the way down,' said the prisoner.

'You said you swallowed it because you were bored,' I said.

'No, doctor, I was picking my teeth with it, and it suddenly slipped down. It wasn't intentional.'

Like his crime, no doubt. The next prisoner was a truly pathetic man, tormented by hallucinations.

'There are seven kinds of worm, doctor,' he said. 'I've probably got flatworm, but I've definitely got tapeworm, because I can hear it talking to me.'

No doubt advances in the parasitological sciences will soon result in a compact-disc worm.

My next visitor was a nonce – a sex offender – who had the misfortune to be middle-class as well. A nonce without a glottal stop is in double jeopardy, and the inmates had lost little time in making their feelings known. A group of six or seven of them had pounced on him when there were no warders present and they had beaten him black and blue.

'I didn't know animals like that existed until I came here,' said the unfortunate man.

I patched him up. He asked me whether what he had experienced was common or unusual.

'Common, I'm afraid,' I said, and did not like to add that it was likely to be repeated unless he volunteered for solitary confinement, it being impossible otherwise to contain the moral outrage of burglars, armed robbers, muggers and arsonists.

Finally, a bull of a man came to see me. He was a notorious gangster who had administered savage beatings to many enemies and had slashed the faces of several young men with a knife. He said he was feeling utterly despondent, and I asked why.

He handed me a letter and I knew without reading it that it was a Dear John – a letter from a wife or girlfriend to say that she was leaving him for good.

The gangster turned his eyes up towards the heavens like the Virgin in a painting by Murillo, and said, 'What have I ever done, doctor, to deserve this?'

# 27

I was called out to a local housing estate last week because a lady was reported to be disturbing her neighbours there at night. As I approached her house, I felt the rhythmic vibration of very loud rock music enter my legs through the pavement. Then I heard a deep crump, like a distant barrage of artillery. Finally, my eardrums began to tingle uncomfortably. In the slums, one measures the volume of sound not in decibels, but on the Richter scale.

No wonder the neighbours are complaining, I thought. One of the worst things about poverty these days is the sheer ubiquity, the inescapability, of rock music: it's enough to drive one mad. Then I discovered the source of the music: a beaten up old car, painted blue and mauve, inhabited by two young black men, one in a knitted woolly cap in the colours of the Ethiopian flag, and the other in a Che Guevara beret. I was rather surprised to discover that they were not the complained about, but the complainants.

'She's out here all fucking night,' they bellowed above the music, 'banging on our doors.'

Then they drove off in a U-turn, tyres squealing, smoke rising from the road in their tracks.

The lady in question came to the door and invited me in. Her home was in some disarray, with old newspapers piled with the washing-up and dirty linen. I could hear next door's radio through the kitchen wall.

'Is there anything wrong?' I asked.

'No,' she said. 'I'm just cooking toad-in-the-hole. I like to experiment.' She cackled.

An evil-looking, pale substance lay on the kitchen table in a baking-tray encrusted with the black detritus of past efforts, among copies of some of our less

66

intellectual magazines for women.

'I gather you go out at night banging on people's doors,' I said.

'I'm preaching to them, that's all,' she replied. 'Like the Lord tells me to.'

'Do you hear him direct?' I asked.

'No, he speaks to me in dreams. I'm one of his apostles.'

'One of the twelve apostles?' I asked.

'Yes, the twelve.'

I suppose there is no intrinsic reason, if you believe in reincarnation, why one of the twelve apostles should not reappear as a woman in Cherry Park Housing Estate, or why, once there, she should not make toad-in-the-hole. I asked whether I could speak to her son in private. She called him down from his room.

He was an immensely fat young man, so fat that the very effort of breathing made him breathless. When he sat on the kitchen stool, his buttocks overflowed it. He wore a T-shirt with a picture of some jet aircraft and the legend SADDAM BUSTERS in two lines on the front, the word BUSTERS disappearing in the deep fold between his stomach and his breasts when he sat.

'Have you noticed anything wrong with your mother recently?' I asked. The drivelling facetiousness of a disc-jockey came through the wall from next door.

'No,' he wheezed. 'We don't see much of each other. I have my own room, like.'

The house seemed too tiny for separate lives. I was suddenly seized by sorrow and pity for the blighted ugliness of so much of our country, for the bleakness of so many of our citizens' lives. Better my patient should believe herself elect of God than see things through my eyes!

'It's all right -
we've pumped the old lady out.'

# 28

It's terrible to be ill, of course, but it's far worse to be a doctor. That's why so many anaesthetists end up sniffing their own gases; why pathologists choose the monastic calm of the morgue; and why microbiologists love their germs and GP's their golf.

I recall a professor of anatomy once remarking that you don't have to be very intelligent to be a doctor. The trouble is that most doctors *are* very intelligent, at least by comparison with the great majority of the human race. Routine soon bores them; the infinite capacity of their patients to grasp the wrong end of the stick exasperates them.

And so they turn to research, or at least some of them do. The reliability of the test tube comes as a relief after the inconsistencies of the patients. And did one really need to undergo years of rigorous training to think of a reason why Mrs Smith's right knee aches when it's raining, but her left when it's foggy? Dealing with people makes you appreciate things.

The research career of most doctors (I am not talk-ing now of scientists by vocation) falls into two phases. The first occurs early, shortly after qualification. The object of this phase is not to extend knowledge, but to produce scientific papers. These are very necessary for climbing the ladder of promotion. An aspirant to a post who has published nothing is a no-hoper, like a pensioner starting ballet classes. Only the number of publications counts, not their quality. Entire journals exist to cater to this flood of career-promoting verbi-age, and if one were designing a system to encourage industrious mediocrity one could do no better. How many mice have been irradiated, how many rabbits 'sacrificed', how many patients unwittingly bled to the point of anaemia by thesis-vampires, in the pursuit of a senior registrarship!

The second phase of a research career starts when a doctor realises that he has climbed as high as he is ever going to in the medical hierarchy, and that the patients he is seeing now are the same as the patients he will be seeing in twenty-five years' time when he retires (doctors who retire early have a longer life expectancy than those who retire late). To keep the brain alive, to avoid existential despair, doctors resort to tinkering at the frontiers of knowledge.

A consultant of my acquaintance is informed by computer whenever a patient is admitted to his hospital with a certain insignificant biochemical abnormality which he has been studying successfully – a paper every six months – for years. When such a patient arrives, the consultant is like a dog with a bone. Unbeknown to the patient, he or she is likely to be kept in hospital two weeks longer than necessary. Once, in the days when I thought I knew the difference between right and wrong, I informed a patient of her fate at the consultant's hands. 'That's all right, dear,' she replied. 'I like it here. What would I be doing at home anyway?'

# 29

In some respects, I am rather like an economist: I don't really understand economics. For example, I once cabled some money to a friend of mine across the Atlantic and he claimed (when the time came for repayment) not to have received it. The money was debited from my account all right, but never – apparently – credited to his. The question I ask is: Where is that money now? What is its ontological status and where did it go, if it went anywhere? I find it all very puzzling.

On the other hand, I know well enough where taxes come from and where they go to. I returned from a brief holiday recently to find a tax demand for £14,000 waiting for me. I had to tell someone about it, so I confided in my physician friend, a man of the utmost financial rectitude. He is also a notable scientist, a wholly rational man, not given to speculations about the para- or supranormal.

'What an amazing coincidence!' he exclaimed.

'Why?' I asked.

To cut a long story short, he had recently been asked by the lawyers of an accused man to act as an expert adviser. The case was a long and complicated one, and he worked 100 hours on the papers of the case, eventually submitting a bill for £7,000, or £70 an hour.

The lawyers phoned him by return, to say that he had grossly undercharged. Since they, the solicitors, charged £100 an hour for the services of an unskilled clerk, it would not do at all for a hospital consultant to charge much less. Would he please amend his bill and charge twice the original sum, that is to say, £14,000?

Now where will the £14,000 come from? The accused, it goes without saying, is a pauper with not a penny to his name. He is on legal aid: thus the £14,000 will come from taxes.

Well, it could be worse. The income on which I am being charged the £14,000 tax is derived from National Health Service medico-legal work; that is to say, from taxes. So the tax on my tax-derived income will pay for my colleague's tax-derived income, which will, of course, be taxed. Thinking about it for too long makes one feel a little dizzy.

I appreciate that it cannot really be the same money just going round and round in ever-decreasing circles. The spiral must be broken somewhere, and some of the money has eventually to be spent on something tangible.

Take, for example, a patient I treated this morning, a young alcoholic. He had reached such a pass that the Department of Social Security gave him a grant of £312 – derived from taxes, naturally – to buy furniture for his rent-rebated council flat. And what could be more tangible than furniture, especially in a flat where the floor served as a bed and the curtains as bedclothes?

Unfortunately, my patient spent his grant not on furniture but on vodka. As a taxpayer, I was outraged by his wilful misuse of public funds – until, that is, I recalled that 90 per cent of the price of a bottle of vodka is . . . tax.

'I'm the fund manager.'

# 30

I realised the situation in the Gulf was serious when Dr V started to speak again to Dr F, something which hadn't happened for several years though they share the same wards. In times of crisis people tend to draw together and forget they cannot agree even on the colour in which the new door to the sluice should be painted. A national emergency brings out the best in people, on the whole.

Of course, quite a lot of twittering went on once it was realised we should have to treat our share of war casualties. The administrator called me and said we had better 'set up a meeting to discuss role type issues'.

'You mean who does what?' I asked.

'More or less,' he replied.

Confidentially, he asked me whether I thought Muslim doctors should be allowed to work with the war-wounded. I said that on the contrary, I thought they ought to be interned in the laundry, with the overspill in the morgue. He took my point, and changed the subject.

Then I had a call from Dr C, who was all of a flutter. Dr C is impeccably left-wing in everything except his own life, and is on principle opposed to all wars except those of national liberation in far away lands of which we know nothing. He asked what we should do about the Gulf. I said that whereof one cannot influence, therefore one must be patient. He supposed I was right, but is probably even now composing a strong letter to the *Guardian*.

The other bastion of radicalism in the hospital, the junior mess, was alive with rumours. Just like the Muslim-owned curry house down the road where I sometimes take my lunch, and where I overhear the conversations of the unemployed and disgruntled lumpenintelligentsia, the junior mess was in daily contact with the Oval Office and CIA headquarters. No secret military code was too complex, no motive too unconscious (at least on the Allied side), for it long to have eluded the geostrategists of the mess. The young and the mad see conspiracies everywhere.

The pacifists didn't have everything their own way, naturally. Ex-army men began to appear from nowhere and to display the leadership qualities to stiffen us civilians with a little moral fibre. They lectured us on high-velocity bullet wounds, on burns and gas and germs; they produced slides to make our hearts miss a beat. They were not bellicose or bloodthirsty, but they enjoyed their moment of moral ascendancy.

A circular arrived. Such and such wards were henceforth reserved for the war-wounded. We must wear our name badges at all times in the hospital, and must show them to the sentries before entering these wards. Where once we feared only drunken hooligans, we now must watch for terrorists.

I know that everyone in our hospital, whatever his private views, will do his duty. I know also that the wartime coalition will break down once the war is over. Dr V will find some reason not to speak to Dr F again.

# 31

The first casualty of the Gulf War was not Truth, but a sixteen-year-old girl who, on the evening hostilities broke out, took a small overdose of painkillers. She did this, she said, because everyone in the world was being so nasty to one another, and because she could not bear to live in a world in which war was possible. All the same, she informed her parents a few moments after she had taken the tablets, and they called the ambulance which brought her to hospital.

No doubt I shall be accused of cynicism, but in my experience grand gestures such as swallowing the contents of the bathroom cabinet are rarely made for reasons of frustrated altruism. I asked the girl for a specific instance of everyone being nasty to one another, and she told me that only a few minutes before she had decided to end it all, her parents had shouted at her for having left the bathroom heater on. This had the unmistakable ring of truth, especially as the girl of her of her own age in the next bed had taken her overdose because her uncle had asked her to switch the television channel they were watching.

Nevertheless, the war has had an undoubted effect on suicidal gestures: they have become uncommon. Our hospital, which deals with more than a thousand such cases a year, admitted only four in the first two weeks of the war, while normally there would have been at least forty. Whatever its disadvantages, war certainly relieves boredom and brings excitement into the drab world of the overdoser. Pills are abjured until the next news bulletin. In wartime, after all, one can not only live vicariously, but die and even kill vicariously.

War, however, brings its own neuroses to civilians. I was asked to visit a 66-year-old man who would not leave his house for fear of being impressed into the forces. He could not be reassured by normal means that his fears were unfounded. He was sitting at home, anxious and trembling, the television relaying to him the latest troop deployments. He asked me whether I thought he would be called up. I said I thought not, and he provided me with a list of physical ailments that would have rendered him a liability on the field of battle.

A few minutes into our conversation, I realised there was something more profoundly wrong with my patient than I had at first suspected. He was confused. In fact, he was beginning to dement. He was living only partly in the present; much of the time, he had returned in his mind to the second world war, and he thought he was still of military age. Saddam was for him a colleague of Rommel.

On the wall of his sitting-room was a portrait of Prince Charles, resplendent in gold-braided uniform, and Princess Diana, coyly regal. I wanted to test his mental faculties further.

'Who are they?' I asked, pointing to the portrait.

He peered at it and thought long and hard.

'I think they're something to do with Ethel,' he replied.

'Who's Ethel?' I asked.

In dementia, islands of memory may be preserved in a sea of forgetfulness.

'My wife, unfortunately.'

'You'll be out of here in no time.'

# 32

I was informed last week by a completely reliable source that in a social services office not far from here it is no longer possible to have a cup of black coffee, though non-white coffee is *de rigueur*. No doubt it took several lengthy meetings to decide the correct (that is to say ethnosensitive) terminology for coffee with and without milk; and it is to such important matters that social workers devote most of their time, which probably explains why it is so infernally difficult to get hold of one on the rare occasions on which it is necessary to do so.

By coincidence, such an occasion arose last week. A patient of mine had struggled manfully with a debilitating disease for some years, but had never given in to it; he ran a small business, selling second-hand ornaments in the market. Eventually, the combination of his disease, the dishonesty of the British public and the thuggery of his competitors (from which the police provided him with no protection at all) defeated him, and he decided to throw himself upon the mercy of the welfare state. He did what he had never done before: he despaired.

As he was increasingly handicapped by his illness, I thought it would only be kind to provide him with as much help as possible, and a social worker would have been able very easily to straighten out a few matters on his behalf. I phoned the department of social work.

The phone rang for a long time, but I knew from experience that this was not necessarily because there was no one in the office. I was right: a somewhat sulky voice answered at last, and I explained what I wanted.

'Today's a strike day,' the voice replied.

I did not enquire how it was that compassion went on strike, for fear of receiving an earful of sub-Marxist rationalisation.

'And when will you be returning to work?' I asked.

'Tomorrow,' she replied.

I asked my patient to come back the following day, when I should find him a social worker to assist him.

Another day, another telephonist. I explained to the new voice what I wanted. She asked for the address of the patient and, on hearing it, said I had come through to the wrong office. She gave me the telephone number of what, in her opinion, was the right office.

The telephonist of the right office, having taken my patient's address, was of the opinion that the first office I had rung was actually the right office. I called back; the telephonist apologised and admitted that she had made a mistake, but unfortunately there was now no one in the office to take my call, but if I called another number, she was sure I should find someone to help me.

I made my fifth phone call in pursuit of a social worker, to discover that the number was that of a general practitioner's surgery. It was true that a social worker went there every alternate Thursday, but he was not expected for another ten days. It was suggested that I try another number.

I made several more calls, without success. Social workers were either in meetings or off sick. At last I was told that my patient's problem did not come within the purview of social services. By this time I had worked out why social workers were so difficult to contact. The people who need them often do not have telephones in their homes, and have to call from public call-boxes. They run out of coins before they can trace their social workers.

Who can blame social workers for avoiding the public? I sometimes resort to similar tactics myself, so I suppose it is a case of the kettle calling the pot b . . . – non-white.

# 33

All professions, except medicine, are conspiracies against the laity, but one is worse than all the others put together. I refer, of course, to the law. For example, when drawing up my will, lawyers translated my half page of clear and generous provisions, expressed in crystalline prose, into six pages of unintelligible gobbledygook, by the end of which I couldn't tell my beneficiaries from my executors. They did this, of course, in the name of clarity.

Lawyers are to language what vandals are to telephone kiosks. I am often called upon to write reports for them about their clients, who claim either compensation for an accident at work or that their vile and criminal behaviour was the result of a subliminal glandular disorder. Naturally, my reports are models of concision and elegance, but the same cannot be said of the letters I receive in return from lawyers.

I examined a man not long ago who fell down a hole at work and has been a nervous wreck ever since. He is suing his employers for negligence. I wrote that there was no doubt his residual symptoms were the result of his accident, but that in such cases it was notoriously difficult to predict how long they would last. Six months later, I received a letter from the lawyer, whose verbal constipation was nearly fatal to his meaning:

> The situation seems to be that Mr G. continues to suffer nightmares the content closely connected with the accident and certainly an inability to function in circumstances which could be a repeat of the experience. You may be aware that there is now recognised as we understand it clinically by psychologists as well as by the judiciary that persons do suffer from post-traumatic stress disorder. Do

you have such experience and if so, can you expand the report in this respect? Is there any possibility of you considering the aspect further as to whether in your view the nightmares are going to be permanent bearing in mind they are still continuing. Could you place some time element on the prognosis that you give?

In other words: Mr G. still has nightmares. Were they caused by the accident? How long will they last?

And another thing about lawyers. They never pay their bills. One firm of solicitors owed me more than £1,000 for reports done a year ago. I wrote them six letters and finally telephoned a partner in the firm. He told me that the accounts department had decreed that all payments should be held up as long as possible because the firm had overspent on office refurbishment. I wrote to the Law Society (who did not reply), and a few days later I received a letter from the partner to whom I had spoken. 'I am sorry you felt it necessary to write to the Law Society. Nevertheless, I hasten to enclose a cheque to you.'

I savoured that richly dishonest *nevertheless*. And if ever he hastens so slowly again, I'll . . . yes, I'll sue him.

# 34

I take it as axiomatic that all men want to be
free: free, that is, of the consequences of their own
actions. When things go well, they praise themselves;
when they go badly, they call a doctor. The function
of the doctor is to furnish excuses, whether to wives
or to courts.

I saw a notable miscreant in the prison last week.
In the old days, absence of mind led to the creation
of the British Empire; nowadays, it leads to indecent
assault. Naturally, the man in question, remanded
on such a charge, remembered nothing, having been
drunk at the material time, but his amnesia did not
prevent him from strenuously asserting his innocence.

His solicitor asked me to examine him because
he had behaved so consistently badly since youth
that his delinquency amounted to *prima facie* evidence
that there was something wrong with him. It is not
normal, said the solicitor, for a boy of nine to set fire
to cats after dousing them with kerosene, or dissolve
live goldfish in sulphuric acid; to which I can only
add, 'What sheltered lives our lawyers lead!'

The young criminal (or victim of circumstance,
according to one's philosophical taste) was called
into the white-tiled consulting room by an old warder,
whose view of humanity had been somewhat darkened
by a life of contact with the utmost villainy. I knew
him of old: he believed that prisoners, being wicked,
were immune to every disease and injury, and that,
in a prisoner, death itself was but the highest form of
malingering.

I find my own cynicism witty and sophisticated;
but in others I find it callous and brutal.

'There must be something wrong with me, doctor,'
said the young man who had the usual scars on his

face and tattoos on his neck.

'Why's that?' I asked.

'Well, I keep doing these things what I don't mean to.'

'Such as?'

'Well, I keep losin' it like, and it's doin' me 'ead in.'

This was psychobabble à la underclass.

'You couldn't be a little more specific, could you?' I asked.

He could. Whenever he and his wife ('common-law, like,' he added) quarrelled, his mind suddenly went blank and he hit her. Sometimes he would grab her by the hair and bash her head against the wall. After several years of such treatment, she had decided to leave him.

'It's doin' me 'ead in, doctor, I can't take no more.'

At the end of my consultation, I told him there was nothing I could do for him.

'Are you saying there's nothing wrong with me?' he asked angrily.

'No, I'm saying there's nothing I can do for you.'

'Well, there's only one thing left for me to do, then,' he said.

He meant suicide, of course; and he thought the prospect of an appearance in the coroner's court was so terrifying to me that I would write him an exculpatory report.

'Anything I do from now on, doctor, it's on your 'ead.'

'No, it isn't,' I said firmly.

On my way out of the prison, I noticed a magnificent black dog held on a short leash by a warder, to discourage prisoners from seeking freedom from the consequences of their own actions.

'Is your dog friendly?' I asked, stroking him.

'Put it like this, sir,' said the warder. 'If this dog was 'uman, 'e'd be in Broadmoor.'

85

# 35

A middle-aged lady appeared in my consulting room last week with a black eye. Her cheek was reddened not by rouge, but by a fist.

'My husband's an agoraholic, doctor,' she said, explaining the provenance of her facial blemishes.

'Then I suppose that you must be alcophobic,' I replied.

My little joke went unheeded, as I intended. But it is a comfort to know that, our economic difficulties notwithstanding, family life in our country continues unchanged.

A young man of sixteen took an overdose last week because it was very cold, he was tired of sleeping rough and it was warm in the hospital. In one way, he was rather remarkable: he knew both his parents and he knew their whereabouts. Unfortunately, neither of them wanted him. They had separated when he was eleven. Initially, he had stayed with his mother, but she had grown bored with him: he interfered too much with her social life. She married young, and wanted to live a bit. He truanted from school for a year, without the school even noticing: in the schools in this district it is presence for a year, not absence, that is unusual.

He went then to live with his father, a man of ungovernable temper and wild appetites, at least in the home. He was another man entirely when he left the confines of his domestic tyranny, becoming at once affable and amenable. He was popular in the local pub, well known for his good humour and willingness to do anyone a favour.

'If he was to come into this room now,' said his son, 'you'd think what a nice bloke. He'd be reasonable with you, butter wouldn't melt in his mouth. That's rubbish: he's a home devil but a street angel, that's what he is.'

Matters grew worse when the father married for a second time. His second wife came with three children by a previous marriage and soon had two more by the second marriage (this being a world in which uncles are sometimes younger than their nephews, sisters are old enough to be the mothers of their brothers, and mothers are young enough to be the sisters of their children). The stepmother conceived a violent and implacable dislike of her stepson and waged war on him. Their flat was small and one day she told him not to return until he had a job and could thus contribute money to the household.

The stepmother in Grimm who in the midst of midwinter told her stepdaughter not to return until she had filled her basket with wild strawberries did not set a more difficult task than this modern stepmother, wild strawberries in the snow-covered forest being no rarer than employment opportunities in the city for barely literate and unskilled sixteen-year-olds.

It is strange how literature sometimes illumines life (or is it the other way round?). I was called last week to a man who had not left his flat for thirty-five years, not since his brother emigrated to Argentina. He had intended to go with him, but for one reason or another was unable to do so. His brother was now the manager of an *estancia*; his brother, back in the grey slums of home, lived with memorabilia of gaucho life on his walls – saddles, lassos, cowhorns and *bolas*. He played only tangos on his old gramophone: the Miss Havisham of the pampas.

'It doesn't matter if you're illiterate -
my writing's illegible.'

# 36

Last Friday, at nine o'clock in the evening, I was eating dinner when the telephone rang. It was the prison: an inmate had coughed up some blood and now had a fever. Would I come in to see him?

I arrived at the prison hospital to find the patient sitting with four warders drinking tea.

'I'm sorry to have to call you out at this time of night, sir,' said one of them.

'The things you have to do for Umanity, sir!' exclaimed another.

'You what?' said the prisoner.

'Umanity,' repeated the second warder. 'You're Uman, aren't you?'

The prisoner, whose few naturally occurring neurones had been disconnected by the synergistic effects of the British diet and the British educational system, looked as vacant as an Albanian carpark.

'That's the trouble with prison, sir,' continued the warder. 'Use words of more than two syllables and you're fucked.'

The prisoner was one of those self-tattooed people who introduce ordinary blue ink into their skins to create an epidermal memento of Mum and Dad, or to apostrophise Love and Hate. It was nearly impossible to take a history from him, and when (ever conscientious) I asked whether there was any TB in the family, he replied that his father had it.

'How long has he had it?' I asked.

'All his life,' he replied.

I grew suspicious. 'Do you know what I mean by TB?' I asked.

He thought for a time and I waited for the answer, as at a supermarket checkout for the total to be rung up.

'No,' he said.

I prescribed some medicine, in syrup form as for a child: his medical record showed that in the past he had failed to take tablets, pretending to swallow them and then hoarding them in his cell.

'While you're here, sir,' said the warder, 'would you mind having a look at Fisher down the strip?'

Prisoners in strip conditions have no clothes (except for a shapeless gown or a pair of baggy shorts) and their cells are without furnishings, to deprive them of the means with which to commit suicide.

En route, we passed the cell of a deaf-mute sex offender who shouted out to us in his incomprehensible verbigeration. One forgets that the truly unfortunate may also commit crimes.

Fisher was indignant over his strip conditions.

'It's depressing down here, doctor,' he said.

He had a point, certainly. His cell looked as though it had been devised by a psychologist conducting experiments on sensory deprivation. A half-eaten meal in a plastic bowl lay on the floor. Neither the bowl nor the accompanying spoon would have been of much assistance in ending it all. I asked him why he had been put in strip conditions. The warder standing next to me answered for him.

'He tried to hang hisself with his shoelaces in court,' he said.

'What, in the dock in front of the judge?' I asked.

'No, in the cells down below, while he was waiting for his case to come up.'

I turned to Fisher.

'So you tried to hang yourself?' I said.

'Yes, but it was a long time ago, doctor.'

'How long?' I asked.

'Last Wednesday.'

# 37

I was on duty at the prison over the Christmas holiday. The iron walkways and old Victorian brickwork were festooned with paper chains and bells of gold and silver foil. There was a Christmas tree on every wing, organ music emanated from the chapel and according to the menu book which I signed, certifying it fit for Home Office consumption, there was turkey and plum pudding for lunch. (Actually the food in prison is much better than in hospital.)

I was accompanied on my rounds by an old warder who told me that this, thank goodness, was his last Christmas on the inside. He was retiring after forty-five years in uniform.

'I expect you've seen some changes in the service,' I said.

'Oh yes, sir,' he replied. 'Cons in them days didn't have no freedom, and they couldn't see a doctor until they was dying.'

We were both lamenting the now irrecoverably lost era of plain common sense when another warder approached us.

'Would you mind seeing a nonce for me, doctor?' he asked. 'He says he can't keep no food down.'

I went to the prisoner's cell. He looked angry rather than ill.

'Everythink goes straight through me,' he said, tracing the passage of food through his entrails with his finger. 'Even the potatoes.'

'How long have you been like this?' I asked.

'Ever since I come here,' he replied. 'You should see the food – I wouldn't give it to a dog.'

'Unfortunately, sir,' said the old warder as we continued our rounds, 'it's true that the nonces get

91

the worst food, the leftovers like. It's the cons what distribute the meals, and they don't like the nonces. We do what we can to stop it, but it still goes on.'

Next I called on a remanded murderer who had refused his breakfast because he said he was innocent of the charge. It was one of those mundane and-the-next-thing-I-knew-doctor-she-was-dead sort of murders. In the good old days, of course, if a man refused his breakfast it was his own affair; nowadays, a doctor is called immediately to pronounce on the matter.

My rounds over, I was on my way out of the prison when I received an urgent call from C Wing. Prisoner Smith, it seemed, had just been PP-nined; could I come at once?

Some of my readers, perhaps, will not be familiar with the verb *to PP-nine*, which may be used in either the active or passive mood, but only – so far as I am aware – in prison. It means to put a PP-9 battery in a sock and then hit someone with it.

I was told by one warder that in certain prisons such batteries are considered too valuable to be put to this use, and tins of mandarin oranges are substituted: hence the alternative expression to mandarin someone.

I need hardly add that the appearance of the prisoner who had been assaulted with a battery was dreadful to behold. He was in debt to the drug barons, it seemed, and this was intended as a warning to him to pay up or else.

A Merry Christmas to all our murderers!

'He's got his father's drink problem.'

# 38

In my experience, criminals hardly ever know what came over them. They ascribe their absence of mind variously to drink, drugs, their childhood, stress and the menopause. The problem for those of us who believe in plain human wickedness as an explanation of criminal behaviour is that criminality is susceptible to statistical analysis, which clearly demonstrates that a bad upbringing is bad for one.

I went to court last week to testify on behalf of a patient of mine who didn't know what came over him. It was during this unfortunate period of amentia that he hit his wife with a brick. The explanation, from the point of view of the defence, was intimately bound up with the poor impression of women he received at the age of four, when his mother ran off with her lover, leaving him to be brought up by his debauched alcoholic father and various local authority children's homes.

The first thing one notices about a criminal trial is – as a Marxist might put it – its class basis. In a nutshell, it is social class I versus social class V. I may be biased, but I prefer it that way: the thought of social class V versus social class I is enough to make my blood run cold. The judge and counsel deliberate on the fine jurisprudential requirements for *mens rea*, watched by the defendant's relatives and friends, who have spiders tattooed on their necks.

My patient, whose profession was drug dealing, was charged with murder. This is a crime of specific intent: that is to say, he must have intended actually to kill or seriously injure her. In claiming loss of memory (as do a third of murderers), he thought he was making it difficult for the court to convict him, and he was not entirely mistaken. At the time of his crime he was drunk, but there was little other evidence as to his mental state at the time. I was called to testify whether his amnesia was genuine.

The greatest fool may easily ask more than the wisest man can tell. Could my patient remember, or couldn't he? It was as much a question for philosophers as doctors, and despite some fierce questioning I insisted that there was no test available to decide between the two possibilities. Prosecuting counsel murmured despairingly, 'Throw physic to the dogs!'

I was in the witness box for some time, and needed a break. I went to the restaurant in the courthouse and sat down with a cup of coffee. A woman approached me.

'Excuse me, doctor,' she said. 'I'm Bert's wife-to-be.'

Bert was the defendant, and I almost said that I thought she wouldn't be seeing a lot of Bert for the next decade or two (which perhaps was just as well).

'Do you really think he can remember, doctor?'

I had the feeling that upon my reply depended the future marriage. Suffice it to say that memory is the kindest faculty. I have a patient who once stabbed a close friend in the chest. He refers to the occasion as 'the night Bill had his accident'.

# 39

I trust it is by now evident that I favour the utmost economy in the public service, which is why I heartily applauded the recent decision of the hospital management to replace our staff canteen with a vending machine. No longer will we – the doctors – have to suffer at lunchtime the agony of watching the canteen staff wade through invisible treacle to record our orders, produce food, take money and deliver change in ergonomically the least efficient fashion known to man. From now on we shall deal with an utterly reliable, clean and practical machine of polished stainless steel and glass.

Of course, there have been one or two teething troubles. The machine has been placed in the former canteen; to prevent patients or other unauthorised persons from vandalising it, a combination lock has been installed in the door. A circular was sent to inform us of the combination number by which to gain entry (4 and 6 pressed together, followed by 8), and we were asked to destroy the circular once we had memorised it. One wouldn't wish it to fall into the wrong hands.

My secretary and I went last week to try out the new machine. I pressed the numbers into the combination lock and then nearly broke my wrist on the immovable door handle. I tried again: same result, or lack of it.

A third time and, wonder of wonders, the door opened before I had time even to try it. It was opened by a member of the old canteen staff, lurking in her old haunt still, who heard my curses when the door did not open as it should have done.

'I'm sorry, doctor,' she said. 'but they sent you the wrong number in the circular. They're sending out the right one soon.' Until then, she would be on duty to let in the misled customers. How emblematic, I thought, of our economic decline: we spend money on machines but continue to employ the labour they are supposed to replace.

My secretary and I approached the vending machine with due reverence. There was a choice of about thirty items, from sandwiches and apples to packets of crisps and whole meals to be reheated and made soggy in the microwave (use of which was free of charge). There was but one problem with extracting food from the machine, which was that it accepted only the correct change. In this, it was perfectly pitiless: not a penny more would it take, and certainly not a penny less. Most of the items cost sums such as 23, 47 or 89 pence. A member of staff who had come for a sandwich ended up with an apple, because that was the only item whose cost fitted her supply of change.

These problems will no doubt soon be overcome. I have every confidence in our excellent catering manager. This morning, we all received another circular from him:

> I have organised a training session for anyone wishing to be instructed on how to operate the new Vending Machine located in the old canteen.

'The food's still inedible –
I can't work the machine.'

# 40

I don't have many fundamental beliefs, but one of them is in the inevitability of hierarchy. Though personally of humble origins, I consider myself very nearly at the top of the human pile: a place which I find inhabited by many pretenders and impostors.

Nowhere is hierarchy more evident that among prisoners. The nonces – sexual offenders – are the untouchables of prison life, but even among them there is a pecking order: rapists are more highly regarded than exhibitionists, who are superior to child molesters.

One day last week I was examining the new arrivals from the courts when I heard that a nonce – in this case, a rapist – had fallen in the shower and cut himself. 'Fallen in the shower' was, of course, a euphemism for 'got punched in the face'.

In the absence of a nonce of lower grade, the other new recruits to the penal system had turned upon him and beaten him up while the warders' backs were turned. Since a squealer is lower even in the prison hierarchy than a child molester, the assaulted rapist would not reveal what had happened to him or who had done it.

As I sewed up his flesh, which had been split to the skull, he asked – to maintain the illusion of an accident – whether many people slipped in the showers, and even managed to manifest outrage that the Home Office should not have provided non-slip flooring. Then he asked how many stitches there were to go.

'This is the last one,' I said.

'I'll be 'anding out a few stitches of my own when I get back out there, doctor,' he said.

I advised him against this course of action, but

he was an old lag and he knew what was what.

But what he couldn't understand was why his girlfriend had suddenly accused him of rape.

'One minute she was all luvvy-duvvy, like,' he said, 'and we was going to Spine togevver. The next minute she was screaming rape and calling the rozzers in.'

He admitted it was possible that, in his habitual drunken state, he might have forced his unwelcome attentions upon her; but what was really despicable, quite beyond the pale, was the involvement of the police.

'There was no need for it,' he said (this time his outrage was genuine enough). 'I mean, she's got free bruvvers and loads of ex-boyfriends. She could've got them to come round and given me a good 'iding, like, wivout getting me into all this trouble.'

'And saved the tax-payer a lot of money,' I added.

'Yeah,' he said, suddenly seeing the whole business from the middle-class point of view.

Sometimes I wonder what prison is for. I was consulted last week by a burglar two days before his release about a small medical matter. It had been his first sentence and I asked him what he thought of prison.

'It's been very educational,' he said.

'You joined the Open University?' I asked.

'No, doctor. Before I came in, I was like them trees out there.' He looked out of the window. 'Green. But now I've made a lot of useful contacts.'

# 41

Like Lord Justice Butler-Sloss, Dr Marietta Higgs and all right-thinking people, I am against the sexual abuse of children, though it has fleetingly crossed my mind that the complete extirpation of such abuse from our green and pleasant land will perhaps prove rather difficult. Indeed, the very attempt to do so by the Torquemadas of our social services might on occasion result in more harm than good.

Last week I was called to see a man who had suddenly become convinced that 'they' were after him. He had barricaded himself and his family into his house, and would answer neither the door nor the telephone. Less than a fortnight before a pair of social workers had called at the house and declared that a denunciation had been received from an unnamed source to the effect that the man had been sexually abusing his daughter.

The daughter was taken away and subjected to torture (for such is the correct characterisation of an interview with the unctuously compassionate bureaucrats of care). Nevertheless, she refused to confess to her father's crimes and was reluctantly returned home. The fact that the family had previously been a close-knit one was regarded as especially suspicious by the social workers; and the community in which the man lived, being a small one, soon got to hear about the accusations.

Never of strong character or intellect, and unable to disperse the Kafkaesque miasma which now enveloped him, the man went mad and was carted off to the local asylum. Could a guilty conscience have made itself plainer?

During my own infrequent moments of paranoia, I have wondered whether child sexual abuse was not an invention of social workers to prove their indispensability to the welfare of society. I discovered how unworthy a thought this was when I visited a department of social services three days ago. While waiting, and having exhausted the deeply condescending posters on the wall of great blacks in history, produced by the Racism Awareness Unit's Education and Development Bureau, I turned to the internal telephone directory. Here are the positions held by the first twenty-five of the eighty people on the list:

Child Care Planning Manager, Supplies Manager, Secretary to Assistant Director of Quality Assurance, Secretary to Service Development Section, Quality Assurance Manager, Informations Systems Support Assistant, Customer Services Manager (Quality Assurance), Operational Support Manager, Service Development Manager, Secretary to Resources Development Manager, Quality Assurance Research Manager, Research Officer (p.m. only and not Thursdays), Information Systems and Technology Manager, Secretary to Assistant Director of Personnel, Principal Planning Manager, Computer Information Systems Organiser, Senior Personnel Manager, Secretary Quality Assurance Section, Secretary (part-time) to Quality Assurance Manager, Administration Manager, Administrative Support Officer, Principal Service Development Manager, Secretary to Assistant Director Family Social Services, Secretary to Operational Support Manager, Assistant Director of Quality Assurance.

I realised at once, of course, that Social Services need no *bonne bouche* like the sexual abuse of children to occupy their time. Indeed, they require no external reality at all. They live in a truly solipsistic world of awareness and sensitivity groups, mutual support meetings and courses on the changing role of social services in a multicultural environment. The wonder is that they can spare a few moments from their busy schedules to drive my patients mad.

'I'd like an opinion in duplicate.'

# 42

I remember reading some years ago a book by Hans Eysenck, the prolific psychologist, in which he suggested that criminality was hereditary, like haemophilia. In those days, before I had the compassion squeezed out of me by daily contact with human folly, I was a liberal, so Eysenck's book infuriated me. Nowadays, I think he may have been half-right after all: if criminality is not hereditary, at the least it is congenital.

I arrived at the prison one afternoon last week at the same time as the visitors. I don't know what they do to their relatives and friends, but by God they frighten me. The women look physically and spiritually squashed, while the men have tattoos on their necks and knuckles, and regard the world with a kind of malevolent jauntiness. And the fact that one knows they've had a hard life, that – in the words of a social worker I know who is given to euphemistic neologisms – they have been differently advantaged, wouldn't help one much if one should happen on them down an alleyway in the dark (not, of course, that one will).

I was given a message as soon as I reached prison hospital.

'Will you go down the Seg., sir, ASAP. There's a Dirty Protest going on.'

A rapist, who went a bit too far and strangled his victim, was in solitary confinement for having called a warder 'a Welsh git'. Seized by the injustice of his treatment, the rapist smashed up the cell and covered himself and the walls with his own excrement (this is what is known as a Dirty Protest). Now he was demanding to see a doctor, that is to say, me.

The ambience in the Seg. had been made worse,

if anything, by the liberal application of Home Office ozone-friendly lavender-scented air freshener. The warders were tramping around in bright pink space suits with gloves, helmets and galoshes, the whole outfit specially designed for Dirty Protests.

'I want you to give me a check-up, doctor,' said the faeces-covered man.

'I'm afraid there's no scientific evidence', I said, 'that periodic check-ups are of any benefit to health.'

'This isn't a real prison,' murmured one of the warders bitterly.

'What's the difference?' I asked.

'In a real prison,' he said, 'they would've got a hose and pinned him against the wall until he'd had enough. He'd soon stop all this shit.'

I returned to the comparative sanity of the prison hospital. There, I admitted the repeated organiser of a paedophile ring. For several years, his sciatica had precluded any physical activity except buggery. Now he had cancer and within three months he would be dead (one tends to forget that recidivists are mortal).

Not being well-versed in the ways of prison, I asked one of the nurses how we dealt with dying prisoners.

'There are two possibilities, sir,' he said. 'He can be released on a special licence, providing you can assure the Home Office he's not fit for anything except dying. Or you can send him to the local general hospital.'

'Can't we look after him here?' I asked.

'Not advisable, sir,' said the nurse.

'Why not?' I asked.

'Well, sir, when a prisoner dies on the in, the paperwork's terrible. It goes on for months, it does.'

# 43

One of the hospital managers gave us a lecture last week on the forthcoming reforms of the Health Service. We've been through reforms before, of course: they're like the epidemics of Asiatic cholera that swept through Europe every ten years or so during the first half of the nineteenth century, terrorising the population. The problem with cholera is that it doesn't leave you immune from the next attack – just like reforms, in fact.

In the past, the reorganisations of the Health Service have in practice been less than fundamental, adding two or three layers to the bureaucracy and giving new titles to old employees. The principal effect in our hospital of one of these reorganisations, as far as I recall, was the appointment of an Auxiliary Services Manager (Laundry), after which my ward suffered a severe shortage of sheets and a huge, indeed overwhelming, surplus of X-ray gowns. But we were assured that the present reforms were altogether more far-reaching in scope.

I must admit that the manager did a good job of explaining what he called the 'philosophy' behind the proposals. They will involve a complete 'culture change', he said: the rigours of market competition will replace the cosy monopoly in medical care that has existed heretofore. At this point, the manager soared effortlessly upwards into the poetic realm of analogy. The relationship between those who held the purse-strings in the brave new Health Service and those who actually provided the medical care would be like the relationship between Marks and Spencer and the manufacturers of their underwear.

According to the manager, the Government had been much impressed by the efficiency of Marks and Spencer when drawing up its reforms of the Health Service, and had used the company as a model. 'What,' interjected a doctor in the audience, 'about our sandwiches?' Could we now look forward to sandwiches of a quality to match Marks and Spencer's at our clinical conferences? Everyone was agreed that if the reforms could do that, there might be something to be said for them after all.

The analogy between doctors and manufacturers of underwear did not please everyone, however. It is not that we doctors have anything against such manufacturers, but we think of our profession in rather more elevated terms. We are learned men, with half-moon spectacles. Besides, we don't want the public complaining about what we do in the way that, presumably, they complain about underwear. Another of the lamentable ideas behind reforms is that doctors should be accountable for what they do (though not to the public, only to accountants).

Speaking for myself, I don't want anyone breathing down my neck, examining whether my patients stay more days than necessary in hospital, fail to get better, are prescribed too many drugs, have to wait too long for an appointment etc. I want to be a free agent, to throw tantrums when I feel like it, to bury my mistakes in silence etc. If I were a Californian, I might say that I want to be me. What's the point of all those years of study and toadying to senior doctors one couldn't abide if, at the end of it all, one still has a boss?

'I'd like to change it for a smaller size.'

# 44

Is there honour among thieves? I am not sure; neither am I sure it would be a good thing if there were. There is undoubtedly a code of conduct among prisoners, though whether honour has anything to do with it, I rather doubt; and grassing up is to this code what genocide is to the Universal Declaration of Human Rights.

But what about honour within thieves? Do they have any?

Last week, I was consulted in prison about a small medical matter by a young British criminal. His charming, almost innocent smile was belied by the words 'Fuck Off' which he had tattooed in small blue letters on his left cheek, and which I should have photographed for my forthcoming book, *The Tattoos of England*, had I had my camera with me.

We discussed his criminal record, which was of impressive length for one so young. He admitted that in what he called his yoof he had been something of a tearaway, though he had never done nothing serious, like, only stolen cars.

'Yes,' he said, 'it was so exciting. I couldn't keep my hands off them. I used to take thirty or forty cars a week.'

I think I must have looked appalled, because he quickly pleaded mitigation.

'I wasn't like some people,' he said. 'I never damaged cars for the sake of it. I never did hand-brake turns at ninety miles an hour, or made the police chase me. I never did much damage to them. I drove them as if they was my own.'

He imitated steering a car, and looked up in an imaginary rear-view mirror.

'Why did you take them?' I asked.

'I just couldn't stop myself, doctor,' he said. 'I had this urge, like.' How long, I thought, before the American Psychiatric Association calls the condition kleptautomobilia? 'If I wanted to go somewhere, I just took a car and when it ran out of petrol, I'd park it quietly at the side of the road and take another one.' (God forbid that he should buy some petrol – the thought never even occurred to him.) 'But I never took no cars with a disabled sticker.'

There spoke the social conscience of modern England. I asked what he would think if he owned a car and it were stolen by some young tyke who wanted to go to the seaside for the day.

'I'd blow his fucking legs off,' he replied.

It was fortunate for him, I remarked, that the British criminal justice system operated on different principles.

'But I'm not into cars no more, doctor. I'm into burgling.'

He was an ethical burglar, however: he never made a mess or deliberately defecated on the carpet, like some of his friends; he just took what he wanted and left. He wouldn't steal from a child's room, nor did he burgle pensioners' houses, and once, when he realised his victims were not prosperous, he left the house empty-handed.

'I only steal from well-off people,' he said.

'Like me,' I said, and I explained that this was not a view with which he could expect me to sympathise deeply.

My next patient in the prison was also a burglar. He had a terrible phobia of flies, such that if he broke into a house and there was a fly in the room, he had to flee.

Reader, I did not treat him. And I shall never swat another fly.

# 45

Prison is a foreign country: they do things differently there.

Thus, a *sterile area* in prison is not, as in hospital, an area free of germs, but an area free of prisoners. I need hardly add that the achievement of asepsis in the penitentiary sense requires precautions as elaborate, in their own way, as those required for asepsis in the medical sense.

Prisoners, of course, are human, only more so. Last week, the first patient in my clinic was a man whom I had seen on the out while he was on bail for a serious crime. He had come to me in the hope that I might declare him unfit to plead, thus postponing indefinitely the evil day of reckoning in court, but I saw no reason to do so in his case. Secretly, I was rather pleased, because he was repulsive and malignant.

'But I never done what they said I done, doctor,' he protested.

'That's not for me to say, I'm afraid,' I replied. 'And whether you did it or not has nothing to do with your fitness to plead. As far as I can tell, you are perfectly well able to challenge jurors, follow the evidence and instruct counsel.'

'But I can't even remember nothing about the day when they said I done it.'

'Then you're not in a very strong position to deny the charges,' I said. 'I'm not a lawyer, but I advise you to change tack.'

'I'm not feeling well,' he said, taking my advice at once and changing tack. 'It's done my head in, all this. I don't know where I am now.'

'Out-patients,' I reminded him.

Needless to say, he wasn't delighted to see me on the in.

'You're the one what got me in here,' he said.

111

'I had nothing to do with it,' I replied firmly. 'I didn't commit the crime, I didn't give evidence in court, I didn't find you guilty and I didn't sentence you.'

'All I wanted was help and you did my head in.'

'There was nothing wrong with you.'

'Well, I'll do my bird – I can 'andle it, bird's never been no problem for me – and then I'll get you.'

I was not in the least worried by his threat, not because it was idle or insincere at the moment it was uttered, but because, by the end of his bird, he will have transferred his affections elsewhere and forgotten all about me.

'Would you like to repeat that in front of an officer?' I said.

'No, I fucking wouldn't,' he said, and stormed out.

Next came a prisoner who was to be released the following day. Prisoners are weighed before they leave the custody of Her Majesty, to prove that they have put on weight, or at least have not lost it, since they were received into her tender hospitality. After this simulacrum of a boxing weigh-in, the doctor customarily asks them whether they are fit (medically speaking) to face the outside world. I haven't known one yet who considered himself unfit.

Next day, however, I met the former prisoner on my ward in the hospital. He had taken an overdose overnight – not a serious or life-threatening one – and he was therefore ready for discharge from hospital by the time I saw him there. To prove himself unfit, he went to the ward lavatory and cut one of his wrists slightly.

'Discharge him, sister,' I said.

'But I might cut my wrists again,' he said.

'You might,' I said.

'Fucking wanker,' he said, and stormed out.

'There you go Mr Tolstoy.'

# 46

Death is a terrible thing, of course, and I advise most
of my readers to have nothing whatever to do with it.
I am glad to report that nearly all my patients take my
advice in this respect, though very occasionally they
choose to disregard it. They have only themselves to
blame for the consequences.

Last week, one of my patients, a very young man
of impulsive character, died suddenly in circumstances
which the coroner found suspicious. I was requested,
therefore, to attend his post mortem at the central
mortuary, an establishment I had not previously visited.

The social atmosphere in this temple of death can
best be described as lugubriously festive. I passed first
through the body storage room, which looked rather
like a large left-luggage department in a station, or a
safe-deposit vault in a bank. We entered the changing
room, on whose notice-board was pinned a photograph of two mortuary attendants, a man and woman,
dressed in bodily fluid-proof aprons and wellington
boots, kissing across an unoccupied dissection table.
The caption read 'Me and my gal'.

The pathologist questioned me closely: when had
I last seen the patient alive, what medicine was he
taking, that kind of thing. In the background hov-
ered a police inspector wearing one of those cheap
suits which look so flashy on the dummy in the shop
window, so crumpled after five minutes' wear.

The pathologist had a stoop: years of bending
over corpses, I suppose. We went into the post-
mortem room itself: two corpses almost covered by
sheets (one with hair exposed, the other with feet)
and my patient, cold and stiff and naked.

'So this is what it all comes to!' I thought to myself,

and all manner of banal philosophical reflections came flooding into my mind.

I had not been to a post mortem for a long time, and had almost forgotten those characteristic post-mortem sounds, the removal of the scalp from the skull by tearing, for example, Raised above us slightly was a gallery with a glass rail, against which was pressed – as a hungry urchin's nose against a restaurant window – the paunch of another police inspector. I looked at his face and knew that I should not care to be a criminal (or a suspect, for that matter) who fell into his hands.

A lot of jokes are told at post mortems, and there is a kind of bonhomie which wards off darker thoughts. A photographer in a gown, a very pretty young woman, snapped anatomical features pointed out by the pathologist. One of the policemen said, 'It's amazing what some people will do to get into a photograph.'

No cause of death was found. There was disappointment all round: we should have to wait now for the toxicology results. There's no doubt that finding a cause lessens everyone's anxiety, even that of small children.

In the hospital corridor I recently overheard a four-year-old boy being told by his parents that his grandmother had died.

'Was she shot or stabbed?' he asked.

# 47

Those who regret their youth plainly forget what it was actually like: all those hormones swirling about in the blood, until one couldn't distinguish one's *Weltschmertz* from one's lust. Youth is disgusting, and that's all there is to it.

Only the other day, an aspiring young intellectual friend of mine asked me whether I read a certain glossy magazine which was read by some horrifying percentage of under-twenty-fives.

'Certainly not,' I replied testily.

'Aren't you interested in the Youth Culture, then?' he asked.

'As far as I'm concerned,' I said loftily, 'youth and culture are entirely antithetical.'

I never thought that I, a member (admittedly reluctant) of the 1968 generation, would sound so soon, or so much, like a retired admiral from the environs of Winchester. Before I am fifty, I shall be denying that earth orbits the sun, or that it is round.

Some of my patients, alas, are youths. Sooner or later, they all seem to take an overdose. They lie in their beds, pouting and challenging one to find out why they did it. Was it because Mama asked them to reduce the volume of their odious music centre, perhaps, or was it because Jason abandoned them for Tracy? 'You tell me, you're supposed to be the doctor,' is a common response. And this from people who say they can't stand authority, which is why they truanted from school. Little bastards!

One day last week there were two of them. I asked them (separately, of course) why they had done it, and despite very different levels of intelligence and education, they replied with identical words:

'Life, the world, everything.'

'You couldn't be a little more specific, could you?' I asked them both. My experience leads me to suppose that the great majority of despair is not caused by the perennially unsatisfactory state of the world, or by philosophical dissatisfaction with the constitution of the universe, but by the small change of daily life, such as the failure of a boyfriend to phone at the appointed hour or by the demand of a parent that a child be home by three in the morning.

The first of the youths expressed the desire – if she survived her overdose, which was very likely, since she took it in the presence of several of her friends – to work with dolphins and whales. Failing that, she wanted to be a nursery nurse.

The second youth was a student of sociology; she was also the Sexual Discrimination Awareness Officer of the students' union. Why had she decided to end it all, when there was so much that remained to be done to make the earth just? It seemed she had quarrelled with her flatmate over the role of the intelligentsia in late capitalist society.

'He called me bourgeois,' she said.

'But that's a compliment,' I said.

'He said all students are bourgeois. And he called me a liberal.'

'The swine!' I muttered.

'I had to move out!'

Thank heavens for middle age! My next patient was of maturer years.

'The trouble with doctors,' he said as he sat down, 'is that they don't understand psychological people like me.'

'You're a picture of National Health,
Mr Perkins.'

# 48

All things considered, it is surprising how many people still believe that organisations such as the Health Service and Social Services exist to bring comfort to the suffering. This, as Dr Johnson might have remarked had he lived in our enlightened times, represents another triumph of hope over experience.

One morning last week, for example, I had a patient who enquired of me about a delicate point of family law. Who better to answer it, I thought, than a hospital social worker? But when I phoned the social work department I was told by the receptionist that all the social workers were in a meeting.

'Well, get one out of the meeting,' I said.

'I can't do that,' she replied, startled by the originality of the idea.

'Why ever not?'

'We never get them out of meetings,' she said. 'It's never done.'

'Is what you are proposing, then, that I send my patient away, and ask her to come back another day, simply because a social worker won't walk ten yards to the phone and answer a question for thirty seconds?'

I think something in my tone of voice must have indicated to her that my wrath was more to be feared than that of a social worker, and she duly interrupted the meeting, with no dire consequences, as far as I am aware, to the welfare of any member of the public.

As for the hospital itself, it is so deeply engaged in its Expenditure Maximisation Programme (EMP) that it hardly has time any more for patients. For example, two of our ward blocks, less than architecturally distinguished I admit, but serviceable nonetheless, were recently extensively redecorated and refurbished. This unaccustomed expenditure on hitherto neglected

119

buildings could only presage demolition, as anyone who has worked in the National Health Service will acknowledge: and so it transpired. No sooner – give or take a month – had the painters and the plumbers departed than the bulldozers moved in. This is a phenomenon I have seen several times in the course of my career: refurbishment as a prelude to extinction. Once it happened to an entire hospital in which I worked. It is, of course, a great comfort to know that all the activity, of the decorators and demolishers alike, counts towards the gross domestic product.

Last week also, I was walking down one of our corridors reflecting on the important if neglected question as to why in National Health hospitals trolleys make such a terrible noise in the corridors while in the private hospitals they don't make any noise at all, when I noticed several large barrows of the kind children in the early nineteenth century used to push in coalmines. The barrows were piled high with the hospital records of thousands of patients.

Being of mildly inquisitive disposition, and always interested in small intellectual puzzles, I asked a passing porter why the patients' notes were thus heaped outside my office.

'Medical records,' he said, 'are moving upstairs into medical illustration.'

'And where is medical illustration moving to?'

In the light of the principles of hospital management outlined above, I shall award no prizes to those who correctly guess the porter's reply.

# 49

Every time I park outside that vast repository of human wickedness, the prison, I notice with mild interest the crunch of shattered glass underfoot, the debris of car windows recently smashed by thieves. When the sun shines, the shards of glass sparkle prettily, like diamonds, as far as the eye can make out the kerb.

In the prison I saw a young robber on his fourth sentence who complained that he couldn't sleep at night. His conscience, perhaps? Not a bit of it: the prison was too far for his girlfriend and nipper to come to visit him, and he was depressed. He hadn't seen them for two weeks and he lay awake at night thinking of them.

'It's a shame you didn't think of that before you committed your crime,' I said sententiously.

'It wasn't me, doctor, it was the drugs.'

The real him wouldn't have dreamt of robbing a post office, but alas, the light of the real him had remained hidden under a bushel of amphetamines for nearly a decade.

It emerged in the course of our conversation that in addition to the girlfriend and nipper who couldn't visit him because of the distance, he had three other girlfriends and nippers who couldn't visit him because of a disinclination to do so.

'Has it ever occurred to you that to father children without being able to care for them is not necessarily a good thing?' I asked.

'It's not me, doctor, it's their mothers what won't let me see them. They say I'm a bad influence.'

'However did they get that impression?' I asked.

'I don't know.'

The worst of it was that he really didn't. Then he thought for a while.

'It must be the drugs, I suppose. They done it.'

'Done what?'

'Made me like this.'

'Isn't anything your fault?'

He shook his head. He couldn't think of anything: a model existence, in fact, apart from circumstance.

Having assured this saintly man a good night's sleep by prescribing some odious brown liquid for him (pills can be spat out later and accumulated for an overdose), I left the prison, only to discover that one of the windows of my car had joined the sparkling glass on the pavement. The perpetrators had then entered my car and rifled through the contents in the vain hope of finding the removable façade of my compact disc player, without which the rest was useless. They declined to steal a thick textbook of forensic psychiatry, sent me for review, worth £125.

And what, had they stolen it, would they have read therein about car theft, the nearest crime in the index to that which they had committed?

> Imprisonment is a frequent disposal for recidivist young car thieves and it may not be totally ineffective: it will certainly prevent offending during detention.

I am sure this would have struck them with the force of revelation, had they but read it. But they would have been more inclined to agree with the following:

> Better, perhaps, to attend specifically to the interests and aspirations of young car thieves.

In short, to reward them for their nefarious activities.

My car has been broken into three times in the last twelve months, at a cost to me of approximately £1,000, and what I want is not prevention or deterrence, but revenge. I shall never prescribe a sleeping draught for a thief again.

'Sorry, I've got compassion fatigue
brought on by too much self pity.'

# 50

When I told a lady in the ward that I knew she drank heavily just by looking at her from the end of the bed, she was stunned.

'Is it as obvious as all that?' she asked.

'I'm afraid it is,' I said. And I could have pointed to the patient in the next bed as a drinker, too.

She, alas, had taken an overdose of painkillers – her fifth such – not to kill herself, but to protest at the refusal of her social worker to visit her after she told him (while drunk) that she was feeling depressed.

'I didn't have no one to talk to,' she said. 'So I took the tablets.'

She was the unmarried mother of nine children. Four had been adopted away at birth, while three were in children's homes. Two, aged three years and eighteen months, lived in her seventeenth-floor council flat. The father of her latest child was 'a good father, like, he comes once a month to see the baby, though he don't talk to me.' His financial contribution to the upkeep of his child was, of course, nil.

She was depressed mainly about pressure on her from the council to take back the three children in children's homes.

'But they don't know what they're like,' she said. 'I can tell them not to do something, but they do it all the same. They behave terrible.' Two of them, aged nine and ten respectively, were already sniffing glue, and last weekend both of them were found dead drunk. 'How can they expect me to look after them?' she asked.

In the afternoon I went to the prison. The first prisoner was on remand and demanded to know why he did things like burglary, because he'd had enough of prison, he didn't need prison, it was doing his head in.

124

'Can you be a little more specific about the things you do?' I asked.

He'd got drunk and then been caught while burgling a house.

'I want to know why I done it, doctor.'

'I expect it was because you were drunk and thought it was a good idea,' I said.

'But there must be some uvver reason, doctor, why I keep doing these things,' he said. 'Because it really hurts my family, and I had a good job, £300 a week take home, and now I've lost it.'

'You want me to tell you that you do these things because at the age of six your mother didn't kiss you enough?'

'That's just it, doctor. She was a very good mother, very loving, like.'

'All right, you do these things because at the age of six your mother kissed you too much.'

'But there's got to be a reason, doctor.'

'What you're really saying to me is this: when you have found the single piece of buried treasure in my psyche that explains my behaviour, I will automatically stop breaking into people's houses; but if you don't find out what it is, which is your job as a doctor, then, when I break into people's houses and steal their videos, it is really your fault and not mine.'

'But there must be a reason, doctor.'

'Furthermore, when I have found the alleged explanation, how are we to know it is the real one, and not a false one? What is the criterion of truth for such an explanation?'

One of the prison officers stepped forward and brought this interesting philosophical dialogue to an end.

'What the doctor's really trying to say to you, son, is *Do your bird*.'

125

# 51

Why can't the English learn their children how to speak?

Only last week I was consulted by an eighteen-year-old man of normal though not brilliant intelligence who had undergone eleven years of compulsory attendance at school (education would be too strong a word for it), at the end of which he was completely unable to read or write. As for arithmetic, it was a closed book to him.

'What is nine times six?' I asked.

A minute of thought and a furrowed brow produced no answer.

'What is three times seven, then?' I asked.

After a lengthy trawl through the deepest recesses of his mind, he eventually came up with an answer:

'Eighteen.'

This suggested at least a subconscious acquaintance with the three times table, insufficient though it undoubtedly was to be of any practical use to him.

I enquired into the methods which had been employed to teach him when he was a young boy. For example, had anyone ever sat him down at a row of desks with other children and taught him his letters?

'No, they never learnt you nothink like that.'

Instead, he and his peers sat around in little groups, which the teachers visited from time to time. But had they not noticed that he was failing to progress?

'Yes. For a time I had special lessons.'

These lessons were soon abandoned. He went back to the normal class, where a friend of his did much of his work for him, and somehow managed to fool the teachers.

'What about your parents?'

'My mother thought I was all right because the

teachers didn't say nothink.'

On leaving school, he managed to find a job as an unskilled labourer, but after a month he was sacked because he couldn't read an instruction. He had remained unemployed since.

He was worried now because he was about to appear in court as a witness in a case involving some of his friends who did not know that he was illiterate and would be humiliatingly unable to read the oath. He feared their derision afterwards: I taught him to recite the oath by heart.

'How have you been able to disguise the fact that you cannot read from them?' I then asked.

Reading, it seemed, did not play a large part in their lives: probably they were the kind of people I meet every day who stumble over big, difficult words like 'thorough' (and it is small differences in attainment which excite the cruellest mockery).

'If they show me a birthday card,' he said, 'I know it's supposed to be funny, so I laugh.'

I asked him about his future.

He didn't know, he took each day as it came. His mother was growing angry with him because he brought no money into the house, but he couldn't claim social security because he couldn't fill in the forms.

'They make you fill them out in front of them.'

'What about learning to read?' I asked. 'It's not too late.'

'No,' he said firmly – he was afraid of being shown up in front of others.

Nevertheless, I phoned the Adult Education Department on his behalf. Alone of all the officials with whom I have to deal, the remedial teachers are genuinely compassionate and eager to help. I explained that my patient was too shy to attend a class, at least initially.

'That's all right,' said the woman teacher. 'I'll
come to his home. We've got many just like him.'

'The Government prefers people
who were born yesterday.'

# 52

In the good old days, social problems were swept under the carpet, where they belong. But now the Government, believing it possible to organise the health service in a rational way, has uncovered by its arrogant bumbling what every doctor has known for a very long time but has never dared to say in public: that old people do not, and cannot, get all the treatment which might be of benefit to them. If they were to get such treatment, practically all other economic activity would have to cease.

Rationing, of course, is best kept invisible, as it was when doctors decided unilaterally who would have what. But now that it is out in the open, with published waiting-lists, medical audit, etc., the way is open for yet further groups of *enragés* to press their claims, which, being unfulfillable, will keep the nation in a permanent state of outraged and embittered effervescence. It used to be possible to tell old folk that they couldn't have physiotherapy because it wouldn't do them any good, and they would probably have believed it; now they know perfectly well that the *real* reason they can't have it is because the middle classes are losing only 40 per cent of their income in taxes.

But even if they were to pay 100 per cent of their incomes in taxes, as not a few in our envy-ridden country would wish, the genie of health-care rationing is now out of the bottle and cannot be returned to it. A sound principle upon which rationing may be based must now be found, whether we like it or not.

All hitherto existing principles have been found wanting. To use age as a basis for rationing is unacceptable: can anyone help being the age they are? Is it not also to play into the hands of a pressure group in the making, the anti-ageists?

It would be far more just to use a criterion over which the individual exercised some control. The one which springs immediately to the mind of anyone who has had prolonged contact with the British public is mannerliness. Far from discriminating against the elderly, it would work in their favour, for two reasons: first, there is a natural tendency for most people to moderate their unpleasantness as they get older, and, second, there has been a continuous deterioration in the British character over the last fifty years.

If the unmannerly are denied treatment, millions – perhaps even billions – could be saved annually. Who knows, perhaps such a scheme would even improve the manners of the British in the long run?

Of course, even if my scheme were implemented, the rich would still be permitted to buy the best care available. A few weeks ago, for example, I met a ninety-year-old lady who was no longer able to look after herself, but would consider going only to the best of the local nursing homes, which charged £35,000 per year. It wouldn't accept her without some indication from her bank as to how long she would be able to keep the payments up. The bank wrote back:

> On the best assumptions we can make about future interest rates, Mrs B— should be able to pay for residence in your nursing home for about the next 200 years.

# 53

If political history is nothing but a tale of crime and folly, what are we to make of medical history? Whenever I read it, I stand amazed that so many intelligent men (I'm talking about doctors, of course) could have believed such manifest absurdities for so long. Reading of the treatment meted out to Louis XIV, Chares II or even George III in the name of therapy is enough to make one's flesh creep. Error and prejudice swayed men's minds for centuries, supported by nothing more than authority.

How fortunate are we who live in an age of reason, when the true causes of disease are known, at least to some of us. When an epidemic strikes, no longer do we see processions of flagellants or penitents bearing miracle-working icons parading through the streets of our cities and accusing Jews of poisoning the wells: on the contrary, we leave everything to the Public Health Laboratory.

It always comes as something of a shock, then, when people display an almost Galenic ignorance of the workings of the body. Last week, for example, I met a man, not otherwise ill-informed or ill-educated, who thought that beer, being watery and yellowish, passed directly into the bladder with which, presumably, he thought the gullet was in direct communication. His surprise at learning otherwise was quite unfeigned, and he went away a much-chastened man.

The patient who followed him was an elderly lady with a minor skin complaint. It is always a good idea for the doctor to have a rounded picture of the patient's life, so I asked her something about her husband.

'Well, doctor,' she said, 'he caught syphilis when his ship was torpedoed in the war, and then it went

131

dormant. When he was made redundant, it woke up again and he's never been the same since.'

I was intrigued by the connection in her mind between the sinking of her husband's ship and syphilis, but I thought that my curiosity should be contained. In this case, better illusion than scientific knowledge.

Prison is another place where one often hears peculiar physiological theories. A man accused of murder consulted me in prison during the same week about a problem with his feet. Having sorted it out, I asked him what he had done to be accused of so heinous a crime.

'The police say I killed her,' he said angrily. 'They're talking rubbish. They don't know what they're talking about. They're just trying to set me up.'

'What did you actually do?' I asked.

'I scratched her throat with a knife.'

My next patient was a man accused of attempted murder.

'Are you going guilty or not guilty?' I asked him.

'Not guilty,' he said. 'I never done it.'

'But you must have done something,' I said.

'I hit my friend with a poker,' he replied.

'Once?' I asked.

'Three times,' he said. 'He's just come out of hospital.'

'I hope you don't mind me asking,' I remarked after a brief pause. 'But if you weren't trying to kill him, what were you trying to do?'

'He's on Bupa.'

# 54

The last time they tried to break into my car, a week ago, it was parked sixty yards from a police station. As it was not round a corner, you could get a clear view of it from the desk sergeant's window. Luckily the thieves must have been interrupted in the course of what burglars call their 'work', for they managed only to get as far as removing the lock from the front passenger door. Of course, it will cost me some money and much inconvenience to repair, but matters could have been worse. I might, for example, have caught them in the act, shouted abuse at them and been charged with threatening behaviour.

I was at the police station examining a man in the cells who had made an unprovoked machete attack on a lady who was waiting on the pavement for a taxi. He had never seen her before. He aimed for her neck ('You're innocent,' he shouted immediately before he struck, 'so I'm going to cut off your head') but fortunately he hit her only on the shoulder, and her injuries were not serious. Asked why he'd done it, he replied – rather like Caligula – 'Because I wanted to see the blood run.' It didn't take long to establish that his thought processes were distinctly unusual.

When I returned to my car and discovered the attempt to break in, I didn't bother to report it to the police: what would have been the point? But the following day, I happened to meet one of the officers who had been on duty, and I mentioned it to him.

'Ah,' he said, 'it must've been the Sneads at number forty-seven what did it.'

Number forty-seven is a hundred yards from the police station, and I suppose I must have been non-plussed by the policeman's matter-of-fact tone. At any rate, my jaw went slack.

'Yes,' he continued. 'It was probably them. *Our* cars are being broken into all the time.'

I laughed, but it was the laughter of desperation. I tried to put myself in the position of the lady who was attacked at random with a machete: will she ever resume her normal life? If it happened to me, I think I should be inclined to withdraw from the world entirely. On the same day, my excellent new secretary told me that her mother had just been attacked as she came out of a shop. She was set upon and beaten to the ground by a young man whom she had never seen before, who proceeded to kick her on the pavement of a busy street in broad daylight. One man came to her aid, but thought better of it when his wife said, 'Come away, it's none of our business.' When the assailant had exhausted himself, he walked – he did not run – away. He is still at liberty.

That same afternoon, I was consulted by a patient who had been set upon by five youths as he tried to withdraw money from a cash dispenser. The machine was out of order, but the assailants at least had the satisfaction of administering a good beating to him. Two weeks previously my patient, who lives in a council flat, had asked neighbours to turn down the volume of their music. They replied to his request by breaking four of his ribs.

This is the way millions of us live now.

# 55

From time to time I am called to testify in court, and I must say it gives me a great deal of pleasure to cook the goose of some of my more obnoxious patients. It is some small revenge for all the abuse they have heaped upon me – and others – over the years.

Last week I appeared in the central magistrates' court, a magnificent Victorian gothic building with one of the Ten Commandments – 'Thou shalt not bear false witness against thy neighbour' – emerging from a gargoyle's mouth. One wouldn't have to have been Sherlock Holmes to pick out most of the miscreants as they waited in the entrance hall for their cases to be called. If the Great Detective were alive today, he would write his monograph not on the varieties of cigar ash, but on the pattern of tattoos on the necks of law-breakers.

My case was listed for ten o'clock, but in the time-honoured tradition of the law's delay I was still waiting at half past midday. However, the tableau which unfolded before me was not without interest, and on one or two occasions touched on matters medical.

Behind me sat two police officers, drinking men I should imagine from the fine lattice of blood vessels on their cheeks and the profile of their abdomens. They viewed the proceedings with unfeigned cynicism. 'It's a real eye-opener, ain't it?' one of them said to me, as the first case – an application for the binding-over of an habitual wife-beater to keep the peace – was adjourned because of what the clerk of the court described as 'a shortage of solicitors, and a shortage of papers'. This, I must say, did not correspond to my first impression of the court, where both papers and solicitors seemed more like a seventh and eighth plague of Egypt than in short supply.

There followed a succession of what may be called Standard British Burglars. The SBB looks on the world with a mixture of stupidity, malevolence and self-righteousness, as though relieving people of their hard-earned property were to right a wrong. The first SBB of the day had escaped from a Youth Custody Centre and had re-offended while on the run. The second was so surprised when the 'matter was withdrawn' (one could see from his eyes that he was guilty) that his mouth fell open.

'He can't believe his luck,' one of the policemen behind me said.

The third looked like a rapist-in-training. He would co-operate neither to sit nor to stand before the magistrate when told to do so, and generally oozed defiance. When remanded in custody, he looked round the court and wouldn't leave the dock.

'He needs helping along,' said one of the policemen.

'He's got an attitude problem,' answered the other.

Then came Flaherty, a middle-aged drunk in a state of some dishevelment, more pathetic than malevolent. His solicitor addressed the court to explain why Flaherty had failed to appear the week before on a charge of being drunk and disorderly.

'He was in hospital to be dried out, madam,' he said to the chief magistrate. Then came a description of all his medical conditions. He needed an operation on his leg, he was taking antibiotics for his chest, his back was bad, he had angina, he had an itchy rash.

'Twenty pounds or a day in prison,' said the magistrate.

Flaherty chose prison. He also addressed the court tearfully. 'I don't want to drink, madam, I know it's no good to me, I want to give up, my wife's a very

good woman and she's had enough.' It was rather
touching.

'He'll be back on the beer tomorrow evening,'
murmured one of the policemen behind me. 'Come
to think of it,' he added after a pause, 'so will we.'

'Mr Herriot?'

# 56

Sometimes I wish that I was not supposed to love humanity: the strain is simply too great. It would be less, of course, if humanity reciprocated in some measure, or met me halfway, but it doesn't. On the contrary, the more one strives to love humanity, the more advantage it takes of one.

I arrived on the ward at the beginning of last week to discover the first ten beds occupied by people who had taken overdoses. I don't deny that they were unhappy: I complain only that they didn't keep their unhappiness decently to themselves. Why involve doctors? Is there no fortitude left?

Four of the patients were alcoholics, and two were hallucinating. One saw snakes with teeth coming towards him while the other thought that the nurses were leopards. He attempted to jump through the window to escape them, but the glass was unbreakable, installed after a prisoner with appendicitis had evaded the two prison warders deputed to guard him by jumping through the window while they watched the Test match on the ward television.

I asked one of the overdosers why he had done it.

'I don't like the heat, doctor,' he replied. 'It got to me, like, so I took the tablets.'

A thousand pounds' worth of medical treatment ensued: it made me proud to be a taxpayer.

After finishing in the ward, I went to the prison. I was talking to one of my medical colleagues there, lamenting the decline, if not the actual fall, of civilisation since our respective childhoods, when an officer burst in and confirmed our worst suspicions.

'Smith's just been slashed up, sir,' he said.

'Was it a razor-blade and toothbrush job?' asked my colleague wearily.

'No, sir,' said the officer. 'A knife job. On the neck, sir.'

The weapon was unusual and of some interest. Slashing up is generally performed in prison with a blade carefully extracted from a Home Office-issue disposable razor and attached to a Home Office-issue toothbrush handle. From where did the assailant obtain his knife? Unfortunately, the victim (a survivor of many attacks, to judge from the scars present on his shaved scalp) was not prepared to talk.

I was in the prison to prepare a report on a man remanded in custody for a serious offence. His solicitor had wondered whether there was a medical explanation for his client's misconduct. The examination was to have been performed at the expense of Legal Aid, but just as I was about to begin my examination. I received a breathless telephone call from the solicitor.

'Don't examine him, doctor,' he said. 'I've discovered that he has means, and therefore he's not entitled to Legal Aid after all. He'll have to pay for everything.'

I told the remanded prisoner, who up till now had been pleasant and amenable, that he was not entitled to Legal Aid because he was deemed to have sufficient means to pay for a lawyer himself. I asked him whether he wished nevertheless to retain his lawyer's services.

'No, I fucking don't,' he said. 'Not if I have to fucking pay for it. Fucking parasite he is.'

'And do you want to pay for this examination?' I asked.

He looked at me with all the considerable malevolence at his command.

'You can fuck off 'n' all,' he replied.

# 57

One evening last week, as I was lying in bed reading about the rise of religious persecution in the eleventh and twelfth centuries (I have always had difficulty distinguishing my Cathars from my Bogomils), the telephone rang.

'It's the prison, sir. I'll just put you through to the nurse in the hospital.'

'Do you know L—, doctor?' she asked.

'I certainly do,' I replied. L— was an ethical thief, in his own estimation, because he had never harmed anybody, only entered their houses and taken their things. He was a bit like a mediaeval heretic, except that he rejected the possession by others, rather than by himself, of worldly goods.

'He claims to have broken a razor blade in two and swallowed the pieces.'

'Oh,' I groaned. 'Why?'

'The usual, I expect,' replied the nurse. Evidently, L— was next to her, because I heard her ask, 'Feeling a little down, were we?' I didn't hear his reply, but the nurse relayed it to me. 'He says he was feeling a little down, doctor.'

People swallow all kinds of things, of course, to alleviate their existential crises. You don't have to be intelligent, articulate or educated to have an existential crisis. That same day I had spoken at length to a young man who had truanted from school because of the allure of the vapours of glue. From thence he had graduated to amphetamines, cocaine, ecstasy, magic mushrooms and LSD.

When he took these drugs, he said, he thought he gained a special insight into the nature of reality. He spoke as a mystic. Unfortunately, the reality which the drugs revealed to him was highly unpleasant. His hallucinations were frightening. Once he had tried to kill himself because of them. It seemed that everything in the world had been created just for his displeasure, and that if he killed himself, he would take the whole evil world with him.

These were somewhat grandiose ideas for a man living on social security in a flat on the eleventh floor of a tower block (or indeed for anyone) to entertain, but I refrained from saying so. Instead, I suggested that he stopped taking drugs.

'My life is shit,' he said in response.

'Your life is no good,' I said, 'because it has no purpose or direction. You don't know what it is to work towards a goal, or to have an interest.'

'But when I take drugs, I seem to understand, everything is clear.'

'An illusion,' I cried.

'I just don't like the feeling what comes with it, that's all. It's hard to explain the experience while you're not having it.'

'If you tried to explain it while you were having it, you'd think you were speaking profundities, but actually you'd be talking rubbish. Give up drugs: you'll achieve nothing that way.'

'But my life don't mean anything to me.'

'That's because you take drugs.'

He looked at me and asked, 'What am I to do?'

I thought of the end of Chekhov's *A Dreary Story*. Katya tells the distinguished but dying professor of medicine, Nikolay Stepanovitch, that she cannot go on living like this, and asks him in desperation what she should do. He suggests lunch.

I, on the other hand, suggest an out-patient appointment.

'You told him to come back
in three weeks.'

# 58

O crime! What liberties are committed in thy name!

Prison is, of course, by far the safest place to be
for a law-abiding citizen like myself. At least I am
protected there from the activities of criminals by
prison officers built like bomb shelters. Whenever I
see the relatives of the prisoners lining up at the gate
to visit, I realise by what a slender thread I hang on
to my wallet, my house remains unburgled or my car
unvandalised. There is no one to protect me outside
of prison. Why, even the three-year-olds already look
like hardened and determined criminals.

They learn their psychopathy young round here,
on their father's knee – quite literally. Last week, I
was listening to a murderer's tale of woe – 'and the
next thing I knew, doctor, she was on the floor and
I was begging her to get up' – when a prison officer
entered the room flushed and out of breath.

'Can you come down the visits, doctor?' he asked.
'There's a sick child there.'

'Excuse me,' I said to the murderer, just as he
was coming to his explanation of how his wife got
on to the floor in the first place. 'I'll be back in a
minute.'

Grabbing a stethoscope and one or two other instru-
ments, I rushed across the yard, patrolled by alsatians,
to the large room in which prisoners sat at tables
across which they spoke to their visitors, desperately
trying to cram as many words as possible into a few
minutes. One prisoner, however, was sitting on a single chair, surrounded by worried looking officers and
with a nine-month-old baby on his lap. The prisoner
was huge, his offspring tiny.

'Sorry to bother you, doctor,' said one of the officers.
'But the mother was visiting Smith when she ran out

and left him holding the baby.'

The baby was sweet, with big bright brown eyes and a little gurgling smile. But the officers were more frightened of its nappies than of a prison riot.

'I don't need a fucking doctor,' said the father. 'I need the fucking welfare officer.'

I returned with relief to my nice polite murderer.

'As I was saying, doctor, me and my missis was having a few rows like . . .'

In the next room I could hear two women officers discussing the recent shocking events in another establishment (as the staff call prison).

'The inmates held her up in the kitchen and grabbed her gold chain,' said one, describing how a woman officer had been mugged by prisoners.

'It's getting as bad as the streets,' said the other.

Well, not quite. Sometimes prison depresses me – or does my head in, in prison parlance – so I went later that day to a bookshop in the city, to reassure myself that a better and more cultured, civilised world existed. But as I walked towards the shop, about six security guards rushed past me, nearly knocking me over, in pursuit of a thief. He fled into a ladies' wear shop and wouldn't come out. The security guards waited for him outside, anticipating with pleasure his inevitable, though possibly violent, capture.

'See you on the in,' I thought as I continued on my way.

The first shelves in the bookshop were dedicated to True Crime.

# 59

Human folly is without beginning or end, thank God, else what should we who are stricken with graphomania have to write about? Perfection, like Switzerland, is all very well in its way, but it is rather boring as a subject for prose. Luckily for me, there is no shortage of folly in my small corner of the universe. Whenever I think I have finally plumbed its depths, a patient obligingly steps forth to renew my faith in man's infinite faculty.

Last week, a young woman was admitted to my ward complaining of severe abdominal pain for which, after extensive investigation, there was no adequate explanation.

There was nothing for it but to talk to her, a step which we doctors were naturally most reluctant to take.

She was only nineteen, but she had two children, both by the same father, Wayne. He, of course, was the psychopath in the ointment. He beat her regularly, although – as she was quick to point out in his defence – not so badly that she had ever required hospital treatment afterwards. The longest he had gone without hitting her was two months.

She was bright and articulate, the efforts of our educational system notwithstanding, and well-mannered also, though her earliest memories were of her brutal stepfather attacking her drunken mother with a knife. She never drank herself, but she recognised at once the similarity between herself and her mother, and her stepfather and her boyfriend.

'He can be very nice sometimes,' she added with a dying fall.

'When he's not hitting you,' I said.

'Yes,' she replied. 'It sounds silly, doesn't it?'

She loved him even as she feared and hated him. His temper was ungovernable, and sometimes he would drag her by the hair from the nearby shop, if he thought she had been away from home too long. (In my area this is considered normal behaviour.)

His violence was now so persistent that she had had enough; she wanted to leave him but dared not do so for fear of his vengeance.

'He's tried to strangle me twice. My daughter screamed while he was doing it.'

'And what did you say afterwards?' I enquired.

'I asked him not to strangle me in front of the children.'

I explained the implications of what she had said and added that there were very few pure victims in the world.

She told me then of the secret diary she kept, with a record of all Wayne's assaults on her. It was written in a secret code of her own devising, which would be easy enough to crack. She kept it under the floorboards so that Wayne should not find it.

'Why do you write it?' I asked.

'So that when Wayne murders me the police will be able to tell that it was him.'

Later that very day I received a call from a solicitor about another of my patients.

'I thought you ought to be aware, doctor,' said the solicitor, 'that your patient Mrs B— has just made a will in which she leaves everything to her husband providing he doesn't murder her, but everything to her nephews and nieces if, as she says is more than likely, he does.'

'It's a rather risky operation.'

# 60

The Minister came to open the new extension to
our ward last week. I arrived too late at the cer-
emony, thank goodness, to hear the nauseatingly
self-congratulatory speeches, and also to witness the
Minister unveiling the little plaque to commemorate
the unveiling of the little plaque by the Minister.
The Chairman of the Health Authority, a retired
local businessman of ruddy complexion, looked as
though he were going to ascend directly to heaven
– which he will soon, if he doesn't modify some of
his habits.

It was very hot in the ward, and not just because
of the large crowd of people who buzzed round the
Minister like wasps round a jamjar. The television
arc-lights were there, giving out a steamy greenhouse
heat. Men with video cameras, doggedly trailed by
sound-recordists, wandered about the ward, capturing
the historic moment for posterity. Eminent physicians
and men of science tried simultaneously to look non-
chalant about being on television and to wave to
their wives at home. The patients, some of whom
had arrived in the ward that same afternoon, looked
distinctly bemused by it all.

Of course, the Minister would not have stooped as
low as to derive political advantage from the occasion,
oh dear no. It was just that, like any normal person
confronted by suffering, he tried to bring a little comfort. That the television cameras and photographers
from the local newspapers happened to be there was,
well, a fortunate coincidence.

The Minister selected a patient, a man who had
swallowed a large dose of weedkiller the week before,
and started to speak to him. The photographers
suggested that the pictures would be more effective

if the patient were sat in a chair beside his bed, and so the patient, connected by a hundred tubes, was manoeuvred laboriously into the chair by the nurses, who otherwise had only walk-on parts. The Minister resumed his chat with the patient who the week before had wished so urgently to die, to the repeated click and flash of the cameras. The patient had never expected, when he took his Weedol, that it would make him famous, and he began to think there might be something to live for after all. He appeared to enjoy his few minutes of fame and glory.

It was a big day, too, for the consultants, who were decked out in their best suits. A minister, even a junior one in a government nearly as suicidal as the weedkiller patient, was still a minister for all that, and doctors recognise power and importance when they see them. And it was a useful opportunity to gauge one's standing in the hospital by the order in which one was called forth to receive the ministerial handshake. It was like the good old days in Russia, when the rise and fall of ministers was measurable only by their proximity to the *vozhd* atop the mummified Lenin's tomb.

As long as the cameras rolled, the Minister did not suffer from compassion fatigue. After the weedkiller patient, he had words of comfort for the nineteen-year-old girl with slashed wrists and two illegitimate children (by different fathers, naturally).

'It's enough to make you cynical, isn't it?' whispered one of my colleagues, referring to the ministerial performance.

'But I'm already cynical,' I replied.